W9-DBZ-253

# MATLAB ®
## STUDENT VERSION

*learning* SIMULINK® 4

Release **12**

**Release 12**
The MathWorks

**How to Contact The MathWorks:**

| | |
|---|---|
| www.mathworks.com | Web |
| comp.soft-sys.matlab | Newsgroup |

| | |
|---|---|
| suggest@mathworks.com | Product enhancement suggestions |
| bugs@mathworks.com | Bug reports |
| doc@mathworks.com | Documentation error reports |

ISBN 0-9672195-4-X

*Learning Simulink*

Printing History: August 1999   First printing   New manual
January 2001   Second printing   Revised for Simulink 4.0 (Release 12)

# Contents

## Introduction

**1**

## Quick Start

**2**

# How Simulink Works

## 3

## Creating a Model

**4**

# Running a Simulation

## 5

# Analyzing Simulation Results

## 6

# Using Masks to Customize Blocks

**7**

# Simulink Debugger

**8**

# Simulink Quick Reference

**A**

**1**

# Introduction

# About the Student Version

MATLAB® and Simulink® are premier software packages for technical computation in education and industry. The MATLAB Student Version provides all of the features of professional MATLAB, with no limitations, and the full functionality of professional Simulink, with model sizes up to 300 blocks. The Student Version gives you immediate access to the high-performance numeric computing, modeling, and simulation power you need.

MATLAB allows you to focus on your course work and applications rather than on programming details. It enables you to solve many numerical problems in a fraction of the time it would take you to write a program in a lower level language. MATLAB helps you better understand and apply concepts in applications ranging from engineering and mathematics to chemistry, biology, and economics.

Simulink, included with the Student Version, is a block diagram tool for modeling and simulating dynamic systems, including controls, signal processing, communications, and other complex systems.

The Symbolic Math Toolbox, also included with the Student Version, is based on the Maple®V symbolic kernel and lets you perform symbolic computations and variable-precision arithmetic.

MATLAB products are used in a broad range of industries, including automotive, aerospace, electronics, environmental, telecommunications, computer peripherals, finance, and medical. More than 400,000 technical professionals at the world's most innovative technology companies, government research labs, financial institutions, and at more than 2,000 universities, rely on MATLAB and Simulink as the fundamental tools for their engineering and scientific work.

## Student Use Policy

This Student License is for use in conjunction with courses offered at a degree-granting institution. The MathWorks offers this license as a special service to the student community and asks your help in seeing that its terms are not abused.

To use this Student License, you must be a student using the software in conjunction with courses offered at degree-granting institutions.

You may not use this Student License at a company or government lab. Also, you may not use it for research or for commercial or industrial purposes. In these cases, you can acquire the appropriate professional or academic version of the software by contacting The MathWorks.

## Differences from the Professional Version

### MATLAB

The MATLAB Student Version provides full support for all language features as well as graphics, external interface and Application Program Interface (API) support, and access to every other feature of the professional version of MATLAB 6.0.

**MATLAB Differences.** There are a few small differences between the Student Version and the professional version of MATLAB:

- The MATLAB prompt in the Student Version is

  EDU>>

- The window title bars include the words

  <Student Version>

- All printouts contain the footer

  Student Version of MATLAB

  This footer is not an option that can be turned off; it will always appear in your printouts.

- On Windows, the Documentation CD must be in your CD-ROM drive to start MATLAB.

## Simulink

This Student Version contains the complete Simulink product, which is used with MATLAB to model, simulate, and analyze dynamic systems.

### Simulink Differences.

- Models are limited to 300 blocks.
- The window title bars include the words
  <Student Version>
- All printouts contain the footer

  `Student Version of MATLAB`

  This footer is not an option that can be turned off; it will always appear in your printouts.

---

**Note** *Using Simulink*, which is accessible from the Help browser, contains all of the Simulink related information in the *Learning Simulink* book plus additional, advanced information.

---

## Symbolic Math Toolbox

The Symbolic Math Toolbox included with this Student Version lets you access all of the functions in the professional version of the Symbolic Math Toolbox except `maple`, `mapleinit`, `mfun`, `mfunlist`, and `mhelp`. For a complete list of all the available functions, see Appendix B, "Symbolic Math Toolbox Quick Reference," in *Learning MATLAB*.

# Obtaining Additional MathWorks Products

Many college courses recommend MATLAB as their standard instructional software. In some cases, the courses may require particular toolboxes, blocksets, or other products. Many of these products are available for student use. You may purchase and download these additional products at special student prices from the MathWorks Store at www.mathworks.com/store.

Some of the toolboxes you can purchase include:

- Communications
- Control System
- Fuzzy Logic
- Image Processing
- Neural Network
- Optimization
- Signal Processing
- Statistics
- Stateflow® (A demo version of Stateflow is included with your Student Version.)

For an up-to-date list of which toolboxes are available, visit the MathWorks Store.

---

**Note** The toolboxes that are available for the MATLAB Student Version have the same functionality as the full, professional versions. However, these student versions will *only* work with the Student Version. Likewise, the professional versions of the toolboxes will *not* work with the Student Version.

---

# Getting Started with Simulink

| What I Want | What I Should Do |
| --- | --- |
| I need to install Simulink. | See Chapter 2, "Installation," in the *Learning MATLAB* book. |
| I want to start Simulink. | **(Microsoft Windows)** Your MathWorks Documentation CD must be in your CD-ROM drive to start MATLAB. Double-click the MATLAB icon on your desktop to start MATLAB. Click the Simulink icon on the toolbar to start Simulink.<br><br>**(Linux)** Enter the `matlab` command to start MATLAB. Click the Simulink icon on the toolbar to start Simulink. |
| I'm new to Simulink and want to learn it quickly. | Start by reading *Learning Simulink*. You'll learn how to model, simulate, and analyze dynamic systems. Since Simulink is graphical and interactive, this book encourages you to use it quickly. You can access the rest of the Simulink documentation through the online help facility (Help). |
| I want to look at some samples of what you can do with Simulink. | There are numerous demonstrations included with Simulink. You can see the demos by selecting **Demos** from the **Help** menu. (Linux users type `demo` at the MATLAB prompt.) There are Simulink demos for simple models, complex models, and advanced products. You also will find a large selection of demos at `www.mathworks.com/demos`. |

# Finding Reference Information

| What I Want | What I Should Do |
|---|---|
| I want to know how to use a specific Simulink block. | Use the online help facility (Help). The Simulink blocks are described in *Using Simulink* (**Simulink -> Using Simulink -> Block Reference**). |
| I want to find a block for a specific purpose but I don't know its name. | There are several choices:<br><br>• See Appendix A, "Simulink Quick Reference," in this book for a list of Simulink blocks.<br><br>• From Help, peruse the "Block Reference" section in *Using Simulink*.<br><br>• Use Index or Search from Help. |
| I want to know what blocks are available in a general area. | Use Help to see the "Block Reference" section in *Using Simulink*, or see Appendix A, "Simulink Quick Reference," in this book for a list of Simulink blocks. |

# Troubleshooting and Other Resources

| What I Want | What I Should Do |
| --- | --- |
| I have a Simulink specific problem I want help with. | Visit the Technical Support section (www.mathworks.com/support) of the MathWorks Web site and search the Knowledge Base of problem solutions. |
| I want to report a bug or make a suggestion. | Use Help or send e-mail to bugs@mathworks.com or suggest@mathworks.com. |

## Documentation Library

Your MATLAB Student Version contains much more documentation than the two printed books, *Learning MATLAB* and *Learning Simulink*. On your CD is a personal reference library of every book and reference page distributed by The MathWorks. Access this documentation library from Help.

**Note** Even though you have the online documentation set for the MathWorks family of products, not every product is available for the MATLAB Student Version. For an up-to-date list of available products, visit the MathWorks Store. At the store you can also purchase printed manuals for the MATLAB family of products.

### Accessing the Online Documentation

Access the online documentation (Help) directly from your Documentation CD. (Linux users should refer to Chapter 2, "Installation," in the *Learning MATLAB* book for specific information on configuring and accessing the online Help from the CD.)

1 Place the CD in your CD-ROM drive.

2 Select **Full Product Family Help** from the **Help** menu.

Help appears in a separate window.

Tutorials and reference
for MATLAB

Tutorials and reference
for Simulink

Tutorials and reference
for Symbolic Math
Toolbox

Tutorials and reference
for Stateflow

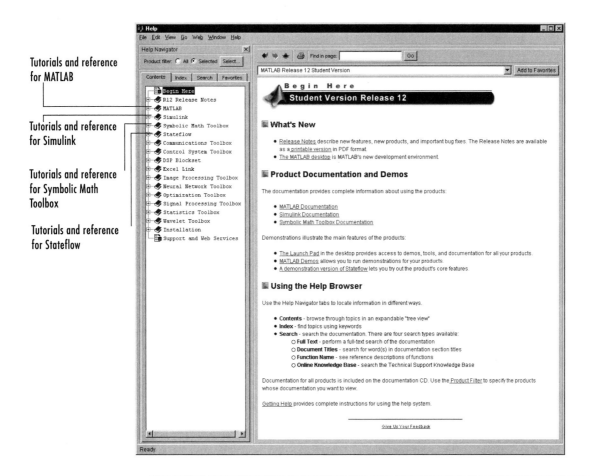

**Note** When you start MATLAB for the first time, the Help Navigator
displays entries for additional products. To learn how to change the displayed
product list, see the "Product Filter" on page 3-10 in *Learning MATLAB*.

## MathWorks Web Site

Use your browser to visit the MathWorks Web site, www.mathworks.com. You'll find lots of information about MathWorks products and how they are used in education and industry, product demos, and MATLAB based books. From the Web site you will also be able to access our technical support resources, view a library of user and company supplied M-files, and get information about products and upcoming events.

## MathWorks Education Web Site

This education-specific Web site, www.mathworks.com/education, contains many resources for various branches of engineering, mathematics, and science. Many of these include teaching examples, books, and other related products. You will also find a comprehensive list of links to Web sites where MATLAB is used for teaching and research at universities.

## MATLAB Related Books

Hundreds of MATLAB related books are available from many different publishers. An up-to-date list is available at www.mathworks.com/support/books.

## MathWorks Store

The MathWorks Store (www.mathworks.com/store) gives you an easy way to purchase add-on products and documentation.

## Usenet Newsgroup

If you have access to Usenet newsgroups, you can join the active community of participants in the MATLAB specific group, comp.soft-sys.matlab. This forum is a gathering of professionals and students who use MATLAB and have questions or comments about it and its associated products. This is a great resource for posing questions and answering those of others. MathWorks staff also participates actively in this newsgroup.

## MathWorks Knowledge Base

You can access the MathWorks Knowledge Base from the Support link on our Web site. Our Technical Support group maintains this database of frequently asked questions (FAQ). You can peruse the Knowledge Base to quickly locate relevant data. You will find numerous examples on graphics, mathematics, API, Simulink, and others. You can answer many of your questions by spending a few minutes with this around-the-clock resource.

## Technical Support

The MathWorks does not provide telephone technical support to users of the MATLAB Student Version. There are numerous other vehicles of technical support that you can use. The "Additional Sources of Information" section in the CD holder identifies the ways to obtain support.

Registered users of the MATLAB Student Version can use our electronic technical support services to answer product questions. Visit our Technical Support Web site at www.mathworks.com/support.

After checking the available MathWorks sources for help, if you still cannot resolve your problem, you should contact your instructor. Your instructor should be able to help you, but if not, there is telephone technical support for registered instructors who have adopted the MATLAB Student Version in their courses.

## Product Registration

Visit the MathWorks Web site (www.mathworks.com/student) and register your Student Version.

# About Simulink

Welcome to Simulink! In the last few years, Simulink has become the most widely used software package in academia and industry for modeling and simulating dynamic systems.

Simulink encourages you to try things out. You can easily build models from scratch, or take an existing model and add to it. Simulations are interactive, so you can change parameters while running a simulation and immediately see what happens. You have instant access to all of the analysis tools in MATLAB, so you can take the results and analyze and visualize them. We hope that you will get a sense of the *fun* of modeling and simulation, through an environment that encourages you to pose a question, model it, and see what happens.

With Simulink, you can move beyond idealized linear models to explore more realistic nonlinear models, factoring in friction, air resistance, gear slippage, hard stops, and the other things that describe real-world phenomena. It turns your computer into a lab for modeling and analyzing systems that simply wouldn't be possible or practical otherwise, whether the behavior of an automotive clutch system, the flutter of an airplane wing, the dynamics of a predator-prey model, or the effect of the monetary supply on the economy.

Simulink is also practical. With thousands of engineers around the world using it to model and solve real problems, knowledge of this tool will serve you well throughout your professional career.

We hope you enjoy exploring the software.

## What Is Simulink?

Simulink is a software package for modeling, simulating, and analyzing dynamic systems. It supports linear and nonlinear systems, modeled in continuous time, sampled time, or a hybrid of the two. Systems can also be multirate, i.e., have different parts that are sampled or updated at different rates.

For modeling, Simulink provides a graphical user interface (GUI) for building models as block diagrams, using click-and-drag mouse operations. With this interface, you can draw the models just as you would with pencil and paper (or as most textbooks depict them). This is a far cry from previous simulation packages that require you to formulate differential equations and difference equations in a language or program. Simulink includes a comprehensive block library of sinks, sources, linear and nonlinear components, and connectors. You can also customize and create your own blocks. For information on creating your own blocks, see the separate *Writing S-Functions* guide in Help.

Models are hierarchical, so you can build models using both top-down and bottom-up approaches. You can view the system at a high level, then double-click on blocks to go down through the levels to see increasing levels of model detail. This approach provides insight into how a model is organized and how its parts interact.

After you define a model, you can simulate it, using a choice of integration methods, either from the Simulink menus or by entering commands in MATLAB's command window. The menus are particularly convenient for interactive work, while the command-line approach is very useful for running a batch of simulations (for example, if you are doing Monte Carlo simulations or want to sweep a parameter across a range of values). Using scopes and other display blocks, you can see the simulation results while the simulation is running. In addition, you can change parameters and immediately see what happens, for "what if" exploration. The simulation results can be put in the MATLAB workspace for postprocessing and visualization.

Model analysis tools include linearization and trimming tools, which can be accessed from the MATLAB command line, plus the many tools in MATLAB and its application toolboxes. And because MATLAB and Simulink are integrated, you can simulate, analyze, and revise your models in either environment at any point.

## What Is Stateflow?

Stateflow is an interactive design tool for modeling and simulating complex reactive systems. Tightly integrated with Simulink and MATLAB, Stateflow provides Simulink users with an elegant solution for designing embedded systems by giving them an efficient way to incorporate complex control and supervisory logic within their Simulink models.

With Stateflow, you can quickly develop graphical models of event-driven systems using finite state machine theory, statechart formalisms, and flow diagram notation. Together, Stateflow and Simulink serve as an executable specification and virtual prototype of your system design. For information on Stateflow, see the *Stateflow User's Guide*, which is accessible from Help.

**Note** Your MATLAB Student Version includes a comprehensive demo version of Stateflow.

# Quick Start

# Running a Demo Model

An interesting demo program provided with Simulink models the thermodynamics of a house. To run this demo, follow these steps:

1 Start MATLAB. See your MATLAB documentation if you're not sure how to do this.

2 Run the demo model by typing thermo in the MATLAB command window. This command starts up Simulink and creates a model window that contains this model.

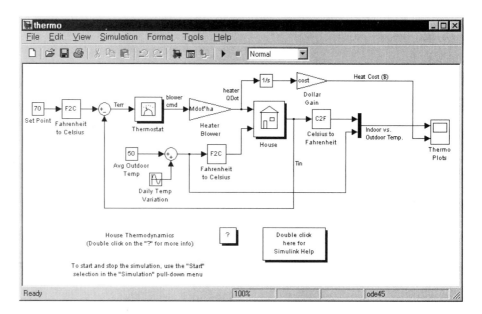

3 Double-click the Scope block labeled Thermo Plots.

The Scope block displays two plots labeled Indoor vs. Outdoor Temp and Heat Cost ($), respectively.

4 To start the simulation, pull down the **Simulation** menu and choose the **Start** command (or, on Microsoft Windows, press the **Start** button on the Simulink toolbar). As the simulation runs, the indoor and outdoor

temperatures appear in the Indoor vs. Outdoor Temp plot and the cumulative heating cost appears in the Heat Cost ($) plot.

**5** To stop the simulation, choose the **Stop** command from the **Simulation** menu (or press the **Pause** button on the toolbar). If you want to explore other parts of the model, look over the suggestions in "Some Things to Try" on page 2-4.

**6** When you're finished running the simulation, close the model by choosing **Close** from the **File** menu.

## Description of the Demo

The demo models the thermodynamics of a house using a simple model. The thermostat is set to 70 degrees Fahrenheit and is affected by the outside temperature, which varies by applying a sine wave with amplitude of 15 degrees to a base temperature of 50 degrees. This simulates daily temperature fluctuations.

The model uses subsystems to simplify the model diagram and create reusable systems. A subsystem is a group of blocks that is represented by a Subsystem block. This model contains five subsystems: one named Thermostat, one named House, and three Temp Convert subsystems (two convert Fahrenheit to Celsius, one converts Celsius to Fahrenheit).

The internal and external temperatures are fed into the House subsystem, which updates the internal temperature. Double-click on the House block to see the underlying blocks in that subsystem.

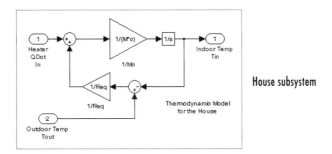

House subsystem

The Thermostat subsystem models the operation of a thermostat, determining when the heating system is turned on and off. Double-click on the block to see the underlying blocks in that subsystem.

 Thermostat subsystem

Both the outside and inside temperatures are converted from Fahrenheit to Celsius by identical subsystems.

 Fahrenheit to Celsius conversion (F2C)

When the heat is on, the heating costs are computed and displayed on the Heat Cost ($) plot on the Thermo Plots Scope. The internal temperature is displayed on the Indoor Temp Scope.

## Some Things to Try

Here are several things to try to see how the model responds to different parameters:

- Each Scope block contains one or more signal display areas and controls that enable you to select the range of the signal displayed, zoom in on a portion of the signal, and perform other useful tasks. The horizontal axis represents time and the vertical axis represents the signal value.

- The Constant block labeled Set Point (at the top left of the model) sets the desired internal temperature. Open this block and reset the value to 80 degrees. See how the indoor temperature and heating costs change. Also, adjust the outside temperature (the Avg Outdoor Temp block) and see how it affects the simulation.

- Adjust the daily temperature variation by opening the Sine Wave block labeled Daily Temp Variation and changing the **Amplitude** parameter.

## What This Demo Illustrates

This demo illustrates several tasks commonly used when building models:

- Running the simulation involves specifying parameters and starting the simulation with the **Start** command, described in "Running a Simulation Using Menu Commands" on page 5-3.

- You can encapsulate complex groups of related blocks in a single block, called a subsystem. See "Creating Subsystems" on page 4-45 for more information.

- You can create a customized icon and design a dialog box for a block by using the masking feature, described in detail in Chapter 7, "Using Masks to Customize Blocks." In the thermo model, all Subsystem blocks have customized icons created using the masking feature.

- Scope blocks display graphic output much as an actual oscilloscope does.

## Other Useful Demos

Other demos illustrate useful modeling concepts. You can access these demos from the Simulink block library window:

**1** Type simulink3 in the MATLAB command window. The Simulink block library window appears.

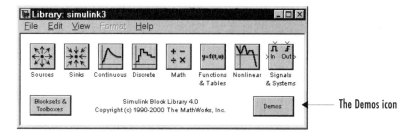

**2** Double-click on the Demos icon. The MATLAB Demos window appears. This window contains several interesting sample models that illustrate useful Simulink features.

# Building a Simple Model

This example shows you how to build a model using many of the model building commands and actions you will use to build your own models. The instructions for building this model in this section are brief. All of the tasks are described in more detail in the next chapter.

The model integrates a sine wave and displays the result, along with the sine wave. The block diagram of the model looks like this.

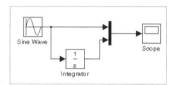

To create the model, first type `simulink` in the MATLAB command window. On Microsoft Windows, the Simulink Library Browser appears.

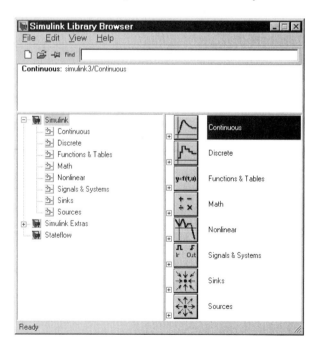

On Linux, the Simulink library window appears.

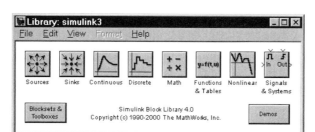

To create a new model on Linux, select **Model** from the **New** submenu of the Simulink library window's **File** menu. To create a new model on Windows, select the **New Model** button on the Library Browser's toolbar.

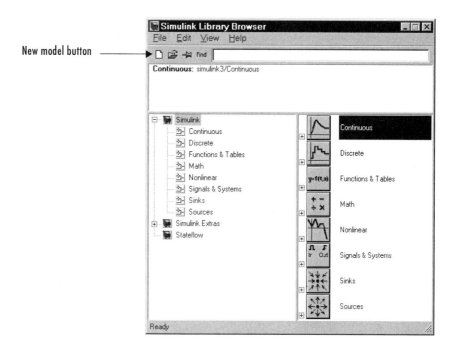

New model button

Simulink opens a new model window.

To create this model, you will need to copy blocks into the model from the following Simulink block libraries:

• Sources library (the Sine Wave block)

• Sinks library (the Scope block)

• Continuous library (the Integrator block)

• Signals & Systems library (the Mux block)

You can copy a Sine Wave block from the Sources library, using the Library Browser (Windows only) or the Sources library window (Linux or Windows).

To copy the Sine Wave block from the Library Browser, first expand the Library Browser tree to display the blocks in the Sources library. Do this by clicking on the Sources node to display the Sources library blocks. Finally click on the Sine Wave node to select the Sine Wave block.

Here is how the Library Browser should look after you have done this.

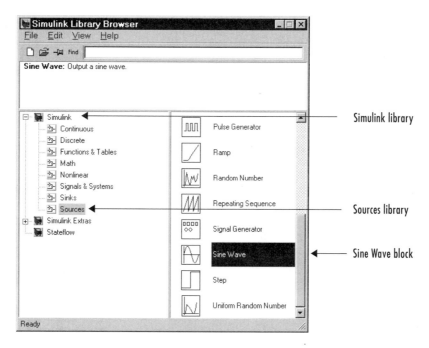

Now drag the Sine Wave block from the browser and drop it in the model window. Simulink creates a copy of the Sine Wave block at the point where you dropped the node icon.

To copy the Sine Wave block from the Sources library window, open the Sources window by double-clicking on the Sources icon in the Simulink library window. (On Windows, you can open the Simulink library window by right-clicking the Simulink node in the Library Browser and then clicking the resulting **Open Library** button.)

Simulink displays the Sources library window.

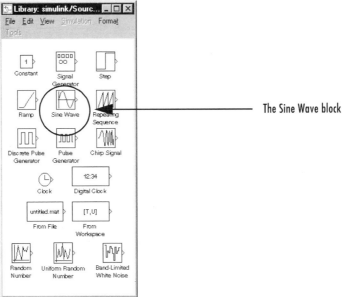

The Sine Wave block

Now drag the Sine Wave block from the Sources window to your model window.

Copy the rest of the blocks in a similar manner from their respective libraries into the model window. You can move a block from one place in the model window to another by dragging the block. You can move a block a short distance by selecting the block, then pressing the arrow keys.

With all the blocks copied into the model window, the model should look something like this.

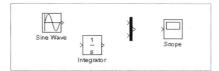

If you examine the block icons, you see an angle bracket on the right of the Sine Wave block and two on the left of the Mux block. The > symbol pointing out of a block is an *output port*; if the symbol points to a block, it is an *input port*. A signal travels out of an output port and into an input port of another block through a connecting line. When the blocks are connected, the port symbols disappear.

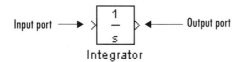

Now it's time to connect the blocks. Connect the Sine Wave block to the top input port of the Mux block. Position the pointer over the output port on the right side of the Sine Wave block. Notice that the cursor shape changes to cross hairs.

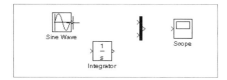

Hold down the mouse button and move the cursor to the top input port of the Mux block.

Notice that the line is dashed while the mouse button is down and that the cursor shape changes to double-lined cross hairs as it approaches the Mux block.

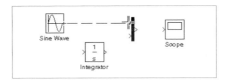

Now release the mouse button. The blocks are connected. You can also connect the line to the block by releasing the mouse button while the pointer is inside the icon. If you do, the line is connected to the input port closest to the cursor's position.

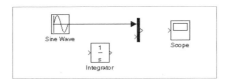

If you look again at the model at the beginning of this section (see "Building a Simple Model" on page 2-6), you'll notice that most of the lines connect output ports of blocks to input ports of other blocks. However, one line connects a *line* to the input port of another block. This line, called a *branch line*, connects the Sine Wave output to the Integrator block, and carries the same signal that passes from the Sine Wave block to the Mux block.

Drawing a branch line is slightly different from drawing the line you just drew. To weld a connection to an existing line, follow these steps:

**1** First, position the pointer *on the line* between the Sine Wave and the Mux block.

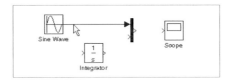

**2** Press and hold down the **Ctrl** key (or click the right mouse button). Press the mouse button, then drag the pointer to the Integrator block's input port or over the Integrator block itself.

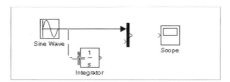

**3** Release the mouse button. Simulink draws a line between the starting point and the Integrator block's input port.

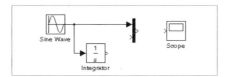

Finish making block connections. When you're done, your model should look something like this.

Now, open the Scope block to view the simulation output. Keeping the Scope window open, set up Simulink to run the simulation for 10 seconds. First, set the simulation parameters by choosing **Simulation Parameters** from the **Simulation** menu.

On the dialog box that appears, notice that the **Stop time** is set to 10.0 (its default value).

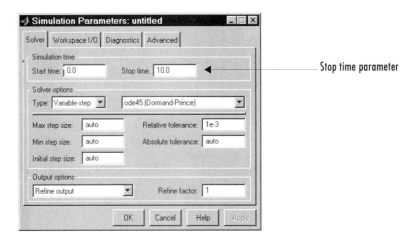

Stop time parameter

Close the **Simulation Parameters** dialog box by clicking on the **OK** button. Simulink applies the parameters and closes the dialog box.

Choose **Start** from the **Simulation** menu and watch the traces of the Scope block's input.

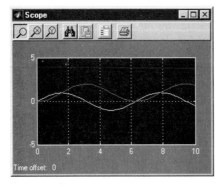

The simulation stops when it reaches the stop time specified in the **Simulation Parameters** dialog box or when you choose **Stop** from the **Simulation** menu or press the **Stop** button on the model window's toolbar (Windows only).

To save this model, choose **Save** from the **File** menu and enter a filename and location. That file contains the description of the model.

To terminate Simulink and MATLAB, choose **Exit MATLAB** (on a Microsoft Windows system) or **Quit MATLAB** (on a Linux system). You can also type quit in the MATLAB command window. If you want to leave Simulink but not terminate MATLAB, just close all Simulink windows.

This exercise shows you how to perform some commonly used model-building tasks. These and other tasks are described in more detail in Chapter 4, "Creating a Model."

# Setting Simulink Preferences

The MATLAB **Preferences** dialog box allows you to specify default settings for many Simulink options. To display the **Preferences** dialog box, select **Preferences** from the Simulink **File** menu.

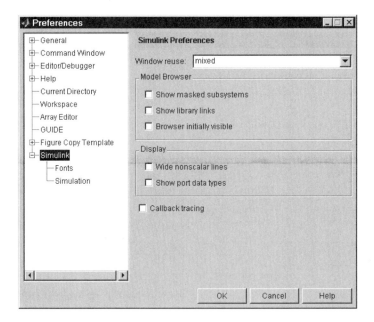

## Simulink Preferences

The **Preferences** dialog box allows you to specify the following Simulink preferences.

### Window reuse

Specifies whether Simulink uses existing windows or opens new windows to display a model's subsystems (see "Window Reuse" on page 4-48).

### Model Browser

Specifies whether Simulink displays the browser when you open a model and whether the browser shows blocks imported from subsystems and the contents of masked subsystems (see "The Model Browser" on page 4-81).

### Display

Specifies whether to use thick lines to display nonscalar connections between blocks and whether to display port data types on the block diagram (see "Setting Signal Display Options" on page 4-38).

### Callback tracing

Specifies whether to display the model callbacks that Simulink invokes when simulating a model (see "Using Callback Routines" on page 4-50).

### Simulink Fonts

Specifies fonts to be used for block and line labels and diagram annotations.

### Solver

Specifies simulation solver options (see "The Solver Pane" on page 5-7).

### Workspace

Specifies workspace options for simulating a model (see "The Workspace I/O Pane" on page 5-17).

### Diagnostics

Specifies diagnostic options for simulating a model (see "The Diagnostics Pane" on page 5-24).

**3**

# How Simulink Works

# What Is Simulink

Simulink is a software package that enables you to model, simulate, and analyze systems whose outputs change over time. Such systems are often referred to as dynamic systems. Simulink can be used to explore the behavior of a wide range of real-world dynamic systems, including electrical circuits, shock absorbers, braking systems, and many other electrical, mechanical, and thermodynamic systems.

Simulating a dynamic system is a two-step process with Simulink. First, you create a graphical model of the system to be simulated, using Simulink's model editor. The model depicts the time-dependent mathematical relationships among the system's inputs, states, and outputs (see "Modeling Dynamic Systems" on page 3-3). Then, you use Simulink to simulate the behavior of the system over a specified time span. Simulink uses information that you entered into the model to perform the simulation (see "Simulating Dynamic Systems" on page 3-8).

# Modeling Dynamic Systems

Simulink provides a library browser that allows you to select blocks from libraries of standard blocks (see the "Block Reference" in the online Simulink help) and a graphical editor that allows you to draw lines connecting the blocks (see Chapter 4, "Creating a Model"). You can model virtually any real-world dynamic system by selecting and interconnecting the appropriate Simulink blocks.

## Block Diagrams

A Simulink block diagram is a pictorial model of a dynamic system. It consists of a set of symbols, called blocks, interconnected by lines. Each block represents an elementary dynamic system that produces an output either continuously (a continuous block) or at specific points in time (a discrete block). The lines represent connections of block inputs to block outputs. Every block in a block diagram is an instance of a specific type of block. The type of the block determines the relationship between a block's outputs and its inputs, states, and time. A block diagram can contain any number of instances of any type of block needed to model a system.

---

**Note** The MATLAB Based Books page on the MathWorks Web site includes texts that discuss the use of block diagrams in general, and Simulink in particular, to model dynamic systems.

---

## Blocks

Blocks represent elementary dynamic systems that Simulink knows how to simulate. A block comprises one or more of the following: a set of inputs, a set of states, and a set of outputs.

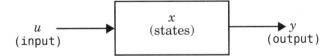

A block's output is a function of time and the block's inputs and states (if any). The specific function that relates a block's output to its inputs, states, and time depends on the type of block of which the block is an instance.

## States

Blocks can have states. A *state* is a variable that determines a block's output and whose current value is a function of the previous values of the block's states and/or inputs. A block that has a state must store previous values of the state to compute its current state. States are thus said to be persistent. Blocks with states are said to have memory because such blocks must store the previous values of their states and/or inputs in order to compute the current values of the states.

The Simulink Integrator block is an example of a block that has a state. The Integrator block outputs the integral of the input signal from the start of the simulation to the current time. The integral at the current time step depends on the history of Integrator block's input. The integral therefore is a state of the Integrator block and is, in fact, its only state. Another example of a block with states is the Simulink Memory block. A Memory block stores the values of its inputs at the current simulation time and outputs them at a later time. The states of a Memory block are the previous values of its inputs.

The Simulink Gain block is an example of a stateless block. A Gain block outputs its input signal multiplied by a constant called the gain. The output of a Gain block is determined entirely by the current value of the input and the gain, which does not vary. A Gain block therefore has no states. Other examples of stateless blocks include the Sum and Product blocks. The output of these blocks is purely a function of the current values of their inputs (the sum in one case, the product in the other). Thus, these blocks have no states.

## System Functions

Each Simulink block type is associated with a set of system functions that specify the time-dependent relationships among its inputs, states, and outputs. The system functions include:

- An output function, $f_o$, that relates the system's outputs to its inputs, states, and time
- An update function, $f_u$, that relates the future values of the system's discrete states to the current time, inputs, and states
- A derivative function, $f_d$, that relates the derivatives of the system's continuous states to time and the present values of the block's states and inputs

Symbolically, the system functions may be expressed as follows

$$y = f_o(t, x, u)$$ Output function

$$x_{d_{k+1}} = f_u(t, x, u)$$ Update function

$$x'_c = f_d(t, x, u)$$ Derivative function

$$\text{where} \quad x = \begin{bmatrix} x_c \\ x_{d_k} \end{bmatrix}$$

where $t$ is the current time, $x$ is the block's states, $u$ is the block's inputs, $y$ is the block's outputs, $x_d$ is the block's discrete derivatives, and $x'_c$ is the derivatives of the block's continuous states. During a simulation, Simulink invokes the system functions to compute the values of the system's states and outputs.

# Block Parameters

Key properties of many standard blocks are parameterized. For example, the gain of Simulink's standard Gain block is a parameter. Each parameterized block has a block dialog that lets you set the values of the parameters when editing or simulating the model. You can use MATLAB expressions to specify parameter values. Simulink evaluates the expressions before running a simulation. You can change the values of parameters during a simulation. This allows you to determine interactively the most suitable value for a parameter.

A parameterized block effectively represents a family of similar blocks. For example, when creating a model, you can set the gain parameter of each instance of the Gain block separately so that each instance behaves differently. Because it allows each standard block to represent a family of blocks, block parameterization greatly increases the modeling power of Simulink's standard libraries.

### Tunable Parameters

Many block parameters are tunable. A *tunable parameter* is a parameter whose value can change while Simulink is executing a model. For example, the gain parameter of the Gain block is tunable. You can alter the block's gain while a simulation is running. If a parameter is not tunable and the simulation is running, Simulink disables the dialog box control that sets the parameter. Simulink allows you to specify that all parameters are nontunable in your model, except for those that you specify. This can speed up execution of large models and enable generation of faster code from your model. See "Model parameter configuration" on page 5–28 for more information.

## Continuous Versus Discrete Blocks

Simulink's standard block set includes continuous blocks and discrete blocks. Continuous blocks respond continuously to continuously changing input. Discrete blocks, by contrast, respond to changes in input only at integral multiples of a fixed interval called the block's sample time. Discrete blocks hold their output constant between successive sample time hits. Each discrete block includes a sample time parameter that allows you to specify its sample rate. Examples of continuous blocks include the Constant block and the blocks in Simulink's Continuous block library. Examples of discrete blocks include the Discrete Pulse Generator and the blocks in the Discrete block library.

Many Simulink blocks, for example, the Gain block, can be either continuous or discrete, depending on whether they are driven by continuous or discrete blocks. A block that can be either discrete or continuous is said to have an implicit sample rate. The implicit sample time is continuous if any of the block's inputs are continuous. The implicit sample time is equal to the shortest input sample time if all the input sample times are integral multiples of the shortest time. Otherwise, the input sample time is equal to the *fundamental sample time* of the inputs, where the fundamental sample time of a set of sample times is defined as the greatest integer divisor of the set of sample times.

Simulink can optionally color code a block diagram to indicate the sample times of the blocks it contains, e.g., black (continuous), magenta (constant), yellow (hybrid), red (fastest discrete), and so on. See "Mixed Continuous and Discrete Systems" on page 3-27 for more information.

## Subsystems

Simulink allows you to model a complex system as a set of interconnected subsystems each of which is represented by a block diagram.You create a subsystem using Simulink's Subsystem block and the Simulink model editor. You can embed subsystems with subsystems to any depth to create hierarchical models. You can create conditionally executed subsystems that are executed only when a transition occurs on a triggering or enabling input (see "Conditionally Executed Subsystems" in the online help for Simulink).

## Custom Blocks

Simulink allows you to create libraries of custom blocks that you can then use in your models. You can create a custom block either graphically or programmatically. To create a custom block graphically, you draw a block diagram representing the block's behavior, wrap this diagram in an instance of Simulink's Subsystem block, and provide the block with a parameter dialog, using Simulink's block mask facility. To create a block programmatically, you create an M-file or a MEX-file that contains the block's system functions (see *Writing S-Functions* in the online help for Simulink). The resulting file is called an S-function. You then associate the S-function with instances of Simulink's S-function block in your model. You can add a parameter dialog to your S-function block by wrapping it in a Subsystem block and adding the parameter dialog to the Subsystem block.

## Signals

Simulink uses the term *signal* to refer to the output values of blocks. Simulink allows you to specify a wide range of signal attributes, including signal name, data type (e.g., 8-bit, 16-bit, or 32-bit integer), numeric type (real or complex), and dimensionality (one-dimensional or two-dimensional array). Many blocks can accept or output signals of any data or numeric type and dimensionality. Others impose restrictions on the attributes of the signals they can handle.

## Solvers

A Simulink model specifies the time derivatives of its continuous states but not the values of the states themselves. Thus, when simulating a system, Simulink must compute continuous states by numerically integrating their state derivatives. A variety of general-purpose numerical integration techniques exist, each having advantages in specific applications. Simulink provides implementations, called ordinary differential equation (ODE) solvers, of the most stable, efficient, and accurate of these numerical integration methods. You can specify the solver to use in the model or when running a simulation.

# Simulating Dynamic Systems

Simulating a dynamic system refers to the process of computing a system's states and outputs over a span of time, using information provided by the system's model. Simulink simulates a system when you choose **Start** from the model editor's **Simulation** menu, with the system's model open.

Simulation of the system occurs in two phases: model initialization and model execution.

## Model Initialization Phase

During the initialization phase, Simulink:

**1** Evaluates the model's block parameter expressions to determine their values.

**2** Flattens the model hierarchy by replacing virtual subsystems with the blocks that they contain (see "Atomic Versus Virtual Subsystems" on page 3-12).

**3** Sorts the blocks into the order in which they need to be executed during the execution phase (see "Determining Block Update Order" on page 3-10).

**4** Determines signal attributes, e.g., name, data type, numeric type, and dimensionality, not explicitly specified by the model and checks that each block can accept the signals connected to its inputs.

Simulink uses a process called attribute propagation to determine unspecified attributes. This process entails propagating the attributes of a source signal to the inputs of the blocks that it drives.

**5** Determines the sample times of all blocks in the model whose sample times you did not explicitly specify.

**6** Allocates and initializes memory used to store the current values of each block's states and outputs.

## Model Execution Phase

The simulation now enters the model execution phase. In this phase, Simulink successively computes the states and outputs of the system at intervals from the simulation start time to the finish time, using information provided by the model. The successive time points at which the states and outputs are computed are called time steps. The length of time between steps is called the step size. The step size depends on the type of solver (see "Solvers" on page 3-12) used to compute the system's continuous states, the system's fundamental sample time (see "Modeling and Simulating Discrete Systems" on page 3-22), and whether the system's continuous states have discontinuities ("Zero Crossing Detection" on page 3-13).

At the start of the simulation, the model specifies the initial states and outputs of the system to be simulated. At each step, Simulink computes new values for the system's inputs, states, and outputs and updates the model to reflect the computed values. At the end of the simulation, the model reflects the final values of the system's inputs, states, and outputs. Simulink provides data display and logging blocks. You can display and/or log intermediate results by including these blocks in your model.

## Processing at Each Time Step

At each time step, Simulink

1 Updates the outputs of the models' blocks in sorted order (see "Determining Block Update Order" on page 3-10).

   Simulink computes a block's outputs by invoking the block's output function. Simulink passes the current time and the block's inputs and states to the output function as it may require these arguments to compute the block's output. Simulink updates the output of a discrete block only if the current step is an integral multiple of the block's sample time.

2 Updates the states of the model's blocks in sorted order.

   Simulink computes a block's discrete states by invoking its discrete state update function. Simulink computes a block's continuous states by numerically integrating the time derivatives of the continuous states. It computes the time derivatives of the states by invoking the block's continuous derivatives function.

**3** Optionally checks for discontinuities in the continuous states of blocks.

Simulink uses a technique called zero crossing detection to detect discontinuities in continuous states. See "Zero Crossing Detection" on page 3-13 for more information.

**4** Computes the time for the next time step.

Simulink repeats steps 1 through 4 until the simulation stop time is reached.

## Determining Block Update Order

During a simulation, Simulink updates the states and outputs of a model's blocks once per time step. The order in which the blocks are updated is therefore critical to the validity of the results. In particular, if a block's outputs are a function of its inputs at the current time step, the block must be updated after the blocks that drive its inputs. Otherwise, the block's outputs will be invalid. The order in which blocks are stored in a model file is not necessarily the order in which they need to be updated during a simulation. Consequently, Simulink sorts the blocks into the correct order during the model initialization phase.

### Direct Feedthrough Blocks

In order to create a valid update ordering, Simulink categorizes blocks according to the relationship of outputs to inputs. Blocks whose current outputs depend on their current inputs are called *direct feedthrough* blocks. All other blocks are called nondirect-feedthrough blocks. Examples of direct-feedthrough blocks include the Gain, Product, and Sum blocks. Examples of nondirect-feedthrough blocks include the Integrator block (its output is a function purely of its state), the Constant block (it does not have an input), and the Memory block (its output is dependent on its input in the previous time step).

## Block Sorting Rules

Simulink uses the following basic update rules to sort the blocks:

- Each block must be updated before any of the direct-feedthrough blocks that it drives.

  This rule ensures that the inputs to direct-feedthrough blocks will be valid when they are updated.

- Nondirect-feedthrough blocks can be updated in any order as long as they are updated before any direct-feedthrough blocks that they drive.

  This rule can be met by putting all nondirect-feedthrough blocks at the head of the update list in any order. It thus allows Simulink to ignore nondirect-feedthrough blocks during the sorting process.

The result of applying these rules is an update list in which nondirect-feedthrough blocks appear at the head of the list in no particular order followed by direct-feedthrough blocks in the order required to supply valid inputs to the blocks they drive.

During the sorting process, Simulink checks for and flags the occurrence of algebraic loops, that is, signal loops in which an output of a direct-feedthrough block is connected directly or indirectly to one of the block's inputs. Such loops seemingly create a deadlock condition since Simulink needs the input of a direct-feedthrough block in order to compute its output. However, an algebraic loop can represent a set of simultaneous algebraic equations (hence the name) where the block's input and output are the unknowns. Further, these equations can have valid solutions at each time step. Accordingly, Simulink assumes that loops involving direct-feedthrough blocks do, in fact, represent a solvable set of algebraic equations and attempts to solve them each time the block is updated during a simulation. For more information, see "Algebraic Loops" on page 3-17.

## Block Priorities

Simulink allows you to assign update priorities to blocks (see "Assigning Block Priorities" on page 4-19). Simulink updates higher priority blocks before lower priority blocks. Simulink honors the priorities only if they are consistent with its block sorting rules.

## Atomic Versus Virtual Subsystems

Subsystems can be virtual or atomic. Simulink ignores virtual subsystem boundaries when determining block update order. By contrast, Simulink executes all blocks within an atomic subsystem before moving onto the next block. Conditionally executed subsystems are atomic. Unconditionally executed subsystems are virtual by default. You can, however, designate an unconditionally executed subsystem as atomic (see Subsystem). This is useful if you need to ensure that a subsystem is executed in its entirety before any other block is executed.

## Solvers

Simulink computes the current value of a block's continuous states by numerically integrating the state's derivatives. The numerical integration task is performed by a Simulink component called a solver. Simulink allows you to choose the solver that it uses to simulate a model. The solvers that Simulink provides fall into two classes: fixed-step solvers and variable-step solvers.

### Fixed-Step Solvers

Fixed-step solvers divide the simulation timespan up into an integral number of fixed-size intervals called time steps. Then, starting from initial estimates, at each time step, a fixed-step solver computes the value of each of the system's state variables at the next time step from the variable's current value and the current value of its derivatives. The accuracy of the estimation depends on the *step size*, that is, the time between successive time steps. Generally, a smaller step size produces a more accurate simulation but results in a longer execution time because more steps are required to compute a system's states.

### Variable Step Solvers

A variable step solver dynamically varies the step size to meet a specified level of precision. Such a solver expands the step size when the state variables are changing slowly (as indicated by the magnitude of the state derivatives) and decreases the step size when the state variables are changing rapidly. A variable step solver can, depending on the application, produce more accurate results without sacrificing execution speed.

### Major Versus Minor Steps

Some solvers subdivide the simulation time span into major and minor steps, where a minor time step represents a subdivision of the major time step. The solver produces a result at each major time step. It use results at the minor time steps to improve the accuracy of the result at the major time step.

## Zero Crossing Detection

When simulating a dynamic system, Simulink checks for discontinuities in the system's state variables at each time step, using a technique known as zero crossing detection. If Simulink detects a discontinuity within the current time step, it determines the precise time at which the discontinuity occurs and takes additional time steps before and after the discontinuity. This section explains why zero crossing detection is important and how it works.

Discontinuities in state variables often coincide with significant events in the evolution of a dynamic system. For example, the instant when a bouncing ball hits the floor coincides with a discontinuity in its position. Because discontinuities often indicate a significant change in a dynamic system, it is important to simulate points of discontinuity precisely. Otherwise, a simulation could lead to false conclusions about the behavior of the system under investigation. Consider, for example, a simulation of a bouncing ball. If the point at which the ball hits the floor occurs between simulation steps, the simulated ball appears to reverse position in midair. This might lead an investigator to false conclusions about the physics of the bouncing ball.

To avoid such misleading conclusions, it is important that simulation steps occur at points of discontinuity. A simulator that relies purely on solvers to determine simulation times cannot efficiently meet this requirement. Consider, for example, a fixed-step solver. A fixed-step solver computes the values of state variables at integral multiples of a fixed step size. However, there is no guarantee that a point of discontinuity will occur at an integral multiple of the step size. You could reduce the step size to increase the probability of hitting a discontinuity, but this would greatly increase the execution time.

A variable step solver appears to offer a solution. A variable step solver adjusts the step size dynamically, increasing the step size when a variable is changing slowly and decreasing the step size when the variable changes rapidly. Around a discontinuity, a variable changes extremely rapidly. Thus, in theory, a variable step solver should be able to hit a discontinuity precisely. The problem is that to locate a discontinuity accurately, a variable step solver must again take many small steps, greatly slowing down the simulation.

## How Zero Crossing Detection Works

Simulink uses a technique known as zero crossing detection to address this problem. With this technique, a block can register a set of zero crossing variables with Simulink, each of which is a function of a state variable that can have a discontinuity. The zero crossing function passes through zero from a positive or negative value when the corresponding discontinuity occurs. At the end of each simulation step, Simulink asks each block that has registered zero crossing variables to update the variables. Simulink then checks whether any variable has changed sign since the last step. Such a change indicates that a discontinuity occurred in the current time step.

If any zero crossings are detected, Simulink interpolates between the previous and current values of each variable that changed sign to estimate the times of the zero crossings (e.g., discontinuities). Simulink then steps up to and over each zero crossing in turn. In this way, Simulink avoids simulating exactly at the discontinuity where the value of the state variable may be undefined.

Zero crossing detection enables Simulink to simulate discontinuities accurately without resorting to excessively small step sizes. Many Simulink blocks support zero crossing detection. The result is fast and accurate simulation of all systems, including systems with discontinuities.

## Implementation Details

An example of a Simulink block that uses zero crossings is the Saturation block. Zero crossings detect these state events in the Saturation block:

- The input signal reaches the upper limit.
- The input signal leaves the upper limit.
- The input signal reaches the lower limit.
- The input signal leaves the lower limit.

Simulink blocks that define their own state events are considered to have *intrinsic zero crossings*. If you need explicit notification of a zero crossing event, use the Hit Crossing block. See "Blocks with Zero Crossings" on page 3-16 for a list of blocks that incorporate zero crossings.

The detection of a state event depends on the construction of an internal zero crossing signal. This signal is not accessible by the block diagram. For the Saturation block, the signal that is used to detect zero crossings for the upper limit is zcSignal = UpperLimit − u, where u is the input signal.

Zero crossing signals have a direction attribute, which can have these values:

- *rising* – a zero crossing occurs when a signal rises to or through zero, or when a signal leaves zero and becomes positive.
- *falling* – a zero crossing occurs when a signal falls to or through zero, or when a signal leaves zero and becomes negative.
- *either* – a zero crossing occurs if either a rising or falling condition occurs.

For the Saturation block's upper limit, the direction of the zero crossing is *either*. This enables the entering and leaving saturation events to be detected using the same zero crossing signal.

If the error tolerances are too large, it is possible for Simulink to fail to detect a zero crossing. For example, if a zero crossing occurs within a time step, but the values at the beginning and end of the step do not indicate a sign change, the solver will step over the crossing without detecting it.

This figure shows a signal that crosses zero. In the first instance, the integrator "steps over" the event. In the second, the solver detects the event.

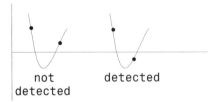

If you suspect this is happening, tighten the error tolerances to ensure that the solver takes small enough steps. For more information, see "Error Tolerances" on page 5–12.

---

**Note** Using the Refine option (see "Refine output" on page 5-15) will not help locate the missed zero crossings. You should alter the maximum step size or output times.

---

## Caveat

It is possible to create models that exhibit high frequency fluctuations about a discontinuity (chattering). Such systems typically are not physically realizable;

a mass-less spring, for example. Because chattering causes repeated detection of zero crossings, the step sizes of the simulation become very small, essentially halting the simulation.

If you suspect that this behavior applies to your model, you can disable zero crossings by selecting the **Disable zero crossing detection** option on the **Advanced** pane of the **Simulation Parameters** dialog box (see "Zero-crossing detection" on page 5-30). Although disabling zero crossing detection may alleviate the symptoms of this problem, you no longer benefit from the increased accuracy that zero crossing detection provides. A better solution is to try to identify the source of the underlying problem in the model.

### Blocks with Zero Crossings

| Block | Description of Zero Crossing |
|-------|------------------------------|
| Abs | One: to detect when the input signal crosses zero in either the rising or falling direction. |
| Backlash | Two: one to detect when the upper threshold is engaged, and one to detect when the lower threshold is engaged. |
| Dead Zone | Two: one to detect when the dead zone is entered (the input signal minus the lower limit), and one to detect when the dead zone is exited (the input signal minus the upper limit). |
| Hit Crossing | One: to detect when the input crosses the threshold. These zero crossings are not affected by the **Disable zero crossing detection** option in the **Advanced** pane of the **Simulation Parameters** dialog box. |
| Integrator | If the reset port is present, to detect when a reset occurs. If the output is limited, there are three zero crossings: one to detect when the upper saturation limit is reached, one to detect when the lower saturation limit is reached, and one to detect when saturation is left. |
| MinMax | One: for each element of the output vector, to detect when an input signal is the new minimum or maximum |

| Block | Description of Zero Crossing  (Continued) |
|---|---|
| Relay | One: if the relay is off, to detect the switch on point. If the relay is on, to detect the switch off point. |
| Relational Operator | One: to detect when the output changes. |
| Saturation | Two: one to detect when the upper limit is reached or left, and one to detect when the lower limit is reached or left. |
| Sign | One: to detect when the input crosses through zero. |
| Step | One: to detect the step time. |
| Subsystem | For conditionally executed subsystems: one for the enable port if present, and one for the trigger port, if present. |
| Switch | One: to detect when the switch condition occurs. |

## Algebraic Loops

Some Simulink blocks have input ports with *direct feedthrough*. This means that the output of these blocks cannot be computed without knowing the values of the signals entering the blocks at these input ports. Some examples of blocks with direct feedthrough inputs are:

- The Math Function block
- The Gain block
- The Integrator block's initial condition ports
- The Product block
- The State-Space block when there is a nonzero D matrix
- The Sum block
- The Transfer Fcn block when the numerator and denominator are of the same order
- The Zero-Pole block when there are as many zeros as poles

To determine whether a block has direct feedthrough, consult the Characteristics table that describes the block in the online Simulink block reference.

An *algebraic loop* generally occurs when an input port with direct feedthrough is driven by the output of the same block, either directly, or by a feedback path through other blocks with direct feedthrough. (See "Nonalgebraic Direct-Feedthrough Loops" on page 3-19 for an example of an exception to this general rule.) An example of an algebraic loop is this simple scalar loop.

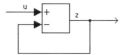

Mathematically, this loop implies that the output of the Sum block is an algebraic state $z$ constrained to equal the first input $u$ minus $z$ (i.e. $z = u - z$). The solution of this simple loop is $z = u/2$, but most algebraic loops cannot be solved by inspection. It is easy to create vector algebraic loops with multiple algebraic state variables $z1$, $z2$, etc., as shown in this model.

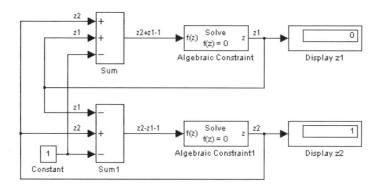

The Algebraic Constraint block is a convenient way to model algebraic equations and specify initial guesses. The Algebraic Constraint block constrains its input signal $F(z)$ to zero and outputs an algebraic state $z$. This block outputs the value necessary to produce a zero at the input. The output must affect the input through some feedback path. You can provide an initial guess of the algebraic state value in the block's dialog box to improve algebraic loop solver efficiency.

A scalar algebraic loop represents a scalar algebraic equation or constraint of the form $F(z) = 0$, where $z$ is the output of one of the blocks in the loop and the function F consists of the feedback path through the other blocks in the loop to the input of the block. In the simple one-block example shown on the previous page, $F(z) = z - (u - z)$. In the vector loop example shown above, the equations are

$$z2 + z1 - 1 = 0$$
$$z2 - z1 - 1 = 0$$

Algebraic loops arise when a model includes an algebraic constraint $F(z) = 0$. This constraint may arise as a consequence of the physical interconnectivity of the system you are modeling, or it may arise because you are specifically trying to model a differential/algebraic system (DAE).

When a model contains an algebraic loop, Simulink calls a loop solving routine at each time step. The loop solver performs iterations to determine the solution to the problem (if it can). As a result, models with algebraic loops run slower than models without them.

To solve $F(z) = 0$, the Simulink loop solver uses Newton's method with weak line search and rank-one updates to a Jacobian matrix of partial derivatives. Although the method is robust, it is possible to create loops for which the loop solver will not converge without a good initial guess for the algebraic states $z$. You can specify an initial guess for a line in an algebraic loop by placing an IC block (which is normally used to specify an initial condition for a signal) on that line. As shown above, another way to specify an initial guess for a line in an algebraic loop is to use an Algebraic Constraint block.

Whenever possible, use an IC block or an Algebraic Constraint block to specify an initial guess for the algebraic state variables in a loop.

## Nonalgebraic Direct-Feedthrough Loops

There are exceptions to the general rule that all loops comprising direct-feedthrough blocks are algebraic. The exceptions are:

- Loops involving triggered subsystems
- A loop from the output to the reset port of an integrator

A triggered subsystem holds its outputs constant between trigger events (see "Triggered Subsystems" in the online Simulink help). Thus, a solver can safely use the output from the system's previous time step to compute its input at the current time step. This is, in fact, what a solver does when it encounters a loop involving a triggered subsystem, thus eliminating the need for an algebraic loop solver.

**Note** Because a solver uses a triggered subsystem's previous output to compute feedback inputs, the subsystem, and any block in its feedback path, can exhibit a one sample-time delay in its output. When simulating a system with triggered feedback loops, Simulink displays a warning to remind you that such delays can occur.

Consider, for example, the following system.

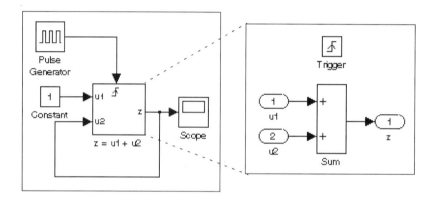

This system effectively solves the equation

```
z = 1 + u
```

where u is the value of z the last time the subsystem was triggered. The output of the system is a staircase function as illustrated by the display on the system's scope.

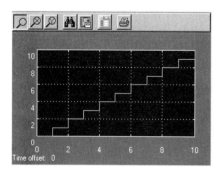

Now consider the effect of removing the trigger from the system shown in the previous example.

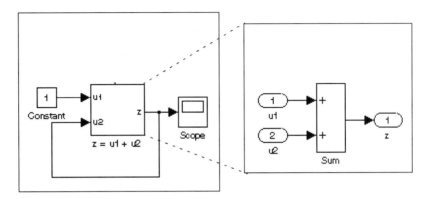

In this case, the input at the u2 port of the adder subsystem is equal to the subsystem's output at the current time step for every time step. The mathematical representation of this system

    z = z + 1

reveals that it has no mathematically valid solution.

# Modeling and Simulating Discrete Systems

Simulink has the ability to simulate discrete (sampled data) systems. Models can be *multirate*, that is, they can contain blocks that are sampled at different rates. Models can also be *hybrid*, containing a mixture of discrete and continuous blocks.

## Discrete Blocks

Each of the discrete blocks has a built-in sampler at its input, and a zero-order hold at its output. When the discrete blocks are mixed with continuous blocks, the output of the discrete blocks between sample times is held constant. The outputs of the discrete blocks are updated only at times that correspond to sample hits.

## Sample Time

The **Sample time** parameter sets the sample time at which a discrete block's states are updated. Normally, the sample time is set to a scalar variable; however, it is possible to specify an offset time (or skew) by specifying a two-element vector in this field.

For example, specifying the **Sample time** parameter as the vector `[Ts,offset]` sets the sample time to `Ts` and the offset value to `offset`. The discrete block is updated on integer multiples of the sample time and offset values only

```
t = n * Ts + offset
```

where `n` is an integer and `offset` can be positive or negative, but less than the sample time. The offset is useful if some discrete blocks must be updated sooner or later than others.

You cannot change the sample time of a block while a simulation is running. If you want to change a block's sample time, you must stop and restart the simulation for the change to take effect.

## Purely Discrete Systems

Purely discrete systems can be simulated using any of the solvers; there is no difference in the solutions. To generate output points only at the sample hits, choose one of the discrete solvers.

## Multirate Systems

Multirate systems contain blocks that are sampled at different rates. These systems can be modeled with discrete blocks or both discrete and continuous blocks. For example, consider this simple multirate discrete model.

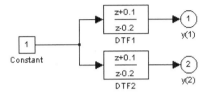

For this example the DTF1 Discrete Transfer Fcn block's **Sample time** is set to [1 0.1], which gives it an offset of 0.1. The DTF2 Discrete Transfer Fcn block's **Sample time** is set to 0.7, with no offset.

Starting the simulation and plotting the outputs using the stairs function

```
[t,x,y] = sim('multirate', 3);
stairs(t,y)
```

produces this plot

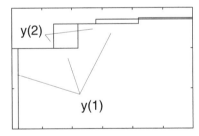

For the DTF1 block, which has an offset of 0.1, there is no output until t = 0.1. Because the initial conditions of the transfer functions are zero, the output of DTF1, y(1), is zero before this time.

## Determining Step Size for Discrete Systems

Simulating a discrete system requires that the simulator take a simulation step at every *sample time hit*, that is, at integral multiples of the system's shortest sample time. Otherwise, the simulator may miss key transitions in the system's states. Simulink avoids this by choosing a simulation step size to ensure that steps coincide with sample time hits. The step size that Simulink chooses depends on the system's fundamental sample time and the type of solver used to simulate the system.

The *fundamental sample time* of a discrete system is the greatest integral divisor of the system's actual sample times. For example, suppose that a system has sample times of 0.25 and 0.5 second. The fundamental sample time in this case is 0.25 second. Suppose, instead, the sample times are 0.5 and 0.75 second. In this case, the fundamental sample time is again 0.25 second.

You can direct Simulink to use either a fixed-step or a variable-step discrete solver to solve a discrete system. A fixed-step solver sets the simulation step size equal to the discrete system's fundamental sample time. A variable-step solver varies the step size to equal the distance between actual sample time hits. The following diagram illustrates the difference between a fixed-step and a variable-size solver.

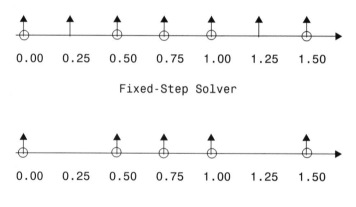

In the diagram, arrows indicate simulation steps and circles represent sample time hits. As the diagram illustrates, a variable-step solver requires fewer simulation steps to simulate a system, if the fundamental sample time is less than any of the actual sample times of the system being simulated. On the other hand, a fixed-step solver requires less memory to implement and is faster if one of the system's sample times is fundamental. This can be an advantage in applications that entail generating code from a Simulink model (using the Real-Time Workshop®).

## Sample Time Propagation

The figure below illustrates a Discrete Filter block with a sample time of Ts driving a Gain block.

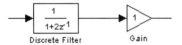

Because the Gain block's output is simply the input multiplied by a constant, its output changes at the same rate as the filter. In other words, the Gain block has an effective sample rate equal to that of the filter's sample rate. This is the fundamental mechanism behind sample time propagation in Simulink.

Simulink sets sample times for individual blocks according to these rules:

- Continuous blocks (e.g., Integrator, Derivative, Transfer Fcn, etc.) are, by definition, continuous.
- The Constant block is, by definition, constant.
- Discrete blocks (e.g., Zero-Order Hold, Unit Delay, Discrete Transfer Fcn, etc.) have sample times that are explicitly specified by the user on the block dialog boxes.
- All other blocks have implicitly defined sample times that are based on the sample times of their inputs. For instance, a Gain block that follows an Integrator is treated as a continuous block, whereas a Gain block that follows a Zero-Order Hold is treated as a discrete block having the same sample time as the Zero-Order Hold block.

  For blocks whose inputs have different sample times, if all sample times are integer multiples of the fastest sample time, the block is assigned the sample time of the fastest input. If a variable-step solver is being used, the block is assigned the continuous sample time. If a fixed-step solver is being used and the greatest common divisor of the sample times (the fundamental sample time) can be computed, it is used. Otherwise continuous is used.

Under some circumstances, Simulink also back propagates sample times to source blocks if it can do so without affecting the output of a simulation. For instance, in the model below, Simulink recognizes that the Signal Generator block is driving a Discrete-Time Integrator block so it assigns the Signal Generator block and the Gain block the same sample time as the Discrete-Time Integrator block.

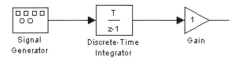

You can verify this by selecting **Sample time colors** from the Simulink **Format** menu and noting that all blocks are colored red. Because the Discrete-Time Integrator block only looks at its input at its sample times, this change does not affect the outcome of the simulation but does result in a performance improvement.

Replacing the Discrete-Time Integrator block with a continuous Integrator block, as shown below, and recoloring the model by choosing **Update diagram** from the **Edit** menu cause the Signal Generator and Gain blocks to change to continuous blocks, as indicated by their being colored black.

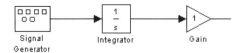

## Invariant Constants

Blocks either have explicitly defined sample times or inherit their sample times from blocks that feed them or are fed by them.

Simulink assigns Constant blocks a sample time of infinity, also referred to as a *constant sample time*. Other blocks have constant sample time if they receive their input from a Constant block and do not inherit the sample time of another block. This means that the output of these blocks does not change during the simulation unless the parameters are explicitly modified by the model user.

For example, in this model, both the Constant and Gain blocks have constant sample time.

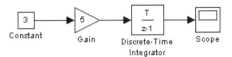

Because Simulink supports the ability to change block parameters during a simulation, all blocks, even blocks having constant sample time, must generate their output at the model's effective sample time.

---

**Note** You can determine which blocks have constant sample time by selecting **Sample Time Colors** from the **Format** menu. Blocks having constant sample time are colored magenta.

---

Because of this feature, *all* blocks compute their output at each sample time hit, or, in the case of purely continuous systems, at every simulation step. For blocks having constant sample time whose parameters do not change during a simulation, evaluating these blocks during the simulation is inefficient and slows down the simulation.

You can set Simulink's inline parameters option (see "Inline parameters" on page 5-28) to remove all blocks having constant sample times from the simulation "loop." The effect of this feature is twofold. First, parameters for these blocks cannot be changed during a simulation. Second, simulation speed is improved. The speed improvement depends on model complexity, the number of blocks with constant sample time, and the effective sampling rate of the simulation.

## Mixed Continuous and Discrete Systems

Mixed continuous and discrete systems are composed of both sampled and continuous blocks. Such systems can be simulated using any of the integration methods, although certain methods are more efficient and accurate than others. For most mixed continuous and discrete systems, the Runge-Kutta variable step methods, ode23 and ode45, are superior to the other methods in terms of efficiency and accuracy. Due to discontinuities associated with the sample and hold of the discrete blocks, the ode15s and ode113 methods are not recommended for mixed continuous and discrete systems.

**4**

# Creating a Model

# Starting Simulink

To start Simulink, you must first start MATLAB. Consult your MATLAB documentation for more information. You can then start Simulink in two ways:

- Click on the Simulink icon 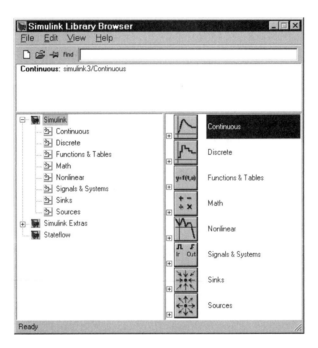 on the MATLAB toolbar.
- Enter the simulink command at the MATLAB prompt.

On Microsoft Windows platforms, starting Simulink displays the Simulink Library Browser.

The Library Browser displays a tree-structured view of the Simulink block libraries installed on your system. You can build models by copying blocks from the Library Browser into a model window (this procedure is described later in this chapter).

On Linux platforms, starting Simulink displays the Simulink block library window.

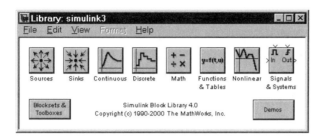

The Simulink library window displays icons representing the block libraries that come with Simulink. You can create models by copying blocks from the library into a model window.

---

**Note** On Windows, you can display the Simulink library window by right-clicking the Simulink node in the Library Browser window.

---

## Creating a New Model

To create a new model, click the **New** button on the Library Browser's toolbar (Windows only) or choose **New** from the library window's **File** menu and select **Model**. You can move the window as you do other windows. Chapter 2, "Quick Start" describes how to build a simple model. "Libraries" on page 4–57 describes how to build systems that model equations.

## Editing an Existing Model

To edit an existing model diagram, either:

- Click the **Open** button on the Library Browser's toolbar (Windows only) or select **Open** from the Simulink library window's **File** menu and then choose or enter the model filename for the model to edit.
- Enter the name of the model (without the .mdl extension) in the MATLAB command window. The model must be in the current directory or on the path.

## Entering Simulink Commands

You run Simulink and work with your model by entering commands. You can enter commands by:

- Selecting items from the Simulink menu bar
- Selecting items from a context-sensitive Simulink menu (Windows only)
- Clicking buttons on the Simulink toolbar (Windows only)
- Entering commands in the MATLAB command window

### Using the Simulink Menu Bar to Enter Commands

The Simulink menu bar appears near the top of each model window. The menu commands apply to the contents of that window.

### Using Context-Sensitive Menus to Enter Commands

Simulink displays a context-sensitive menu when you click the right mouse button over a model or block library window. The contents of the menu depend on whether a block is selected. If a block is selected, the menu displays commands that apply only to the selected block. If no block is selected, the menu displays commands that apply to a model or library as a whole.

### Using the Simulink Toolbar to Enter Commands

Model windows in the Windows version of Simulink optionally display a toolbar beneath the Simulink menu bar. To display the toolbar, check the **Toolbar** option on the Simulink **View** menu.

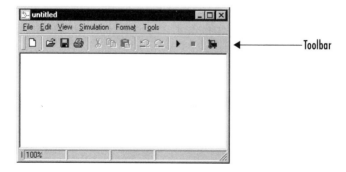

The toolbar contains buttons corresponding to frequently used Simulink commands, such as those for opening, running, and closing models. You can run such commands by clicking on the corresponding button. For example, to open a Simulink model, click on the button containing the open folder icon. You can determine which command a button executes by moving the mouse pointer over the button. A small window appears containing text that describes the button. The window is called a tooltip. Each button on the toolbar displays a tooltip when the mouse pointer hovers over it. You can hide the toolbar by unchecking the **Toolbar** option on the Simulink **View** menu.

### Using the MATLAB Window to Enter Commands

When you run a simulation and analyze its results, you can enter MATLAB commands in the MATLAB command window. Running a simulation is discussed in Chapter 5, and analyzing simulation results is discussed in Chapter 6, "Analyzing Simulation Results."

### Undoing a Command

You can cancel the effects of up to 101 consecutive operations by choosing **Undo** from the **Edit** menu. You can undo these operations:

- Adding or deleting a block
- Adding or deleting a line
- Adding or deleting a model annotation
- Editing a block name
- Creating a subsystem

You can reverse the effects of an **Undo** command by choosing **Redo** from the **Edit** menu.

## Simulink Windows

Simulink uses separate windows to display a block library browser, a block library, a model, and graphical (scope) simulation output. These windows are not MATLAB figure windows and cannot be manipulated using Handle Graphics® commands.

Simulink windows are sized to accommodate the most common screen resolutions available. If you have a monitor with exceptionally high or low resolution, you may find the window sizes too small or too large. If this is the case, resize the window and save the model to preserve the new window dimensions.

## Status Bar

The Windows version of Simulink displays a status bar at the bottom of each model and library window.

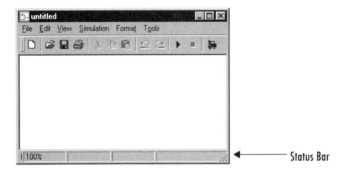

Status Bar

When a simulation is running, the status bar displays the status of the simulation, including the current simulation time and the name of the current solver. You can display or hide the status bar by checking or unchecking the **Status Bar** option on the Simulink **View** menu.

## Zooming Block Diagrams

Simulink allows you to enlarge or shrink the view of the block diagram in the current Simulink window. To zoom a view:

- Select **Zoom In** from the **View** menu (or type r) to enlarge the view.
- Select **Zoom Out** from the **View** menu (or type v) to shrink the view.
- Select **Fit System to View** from the **View** menu (or press the space bar) to fit the diagram to the view.
- Select **Normal** from the **View** menu to view the diagram at actual size.

By default, Simulink fits a block diagram to view when you open the diagram either in the model browser's content pane or in a separate window. If you change a diagram's zoom setting, Simulink saves the setting when you close the diagram and restores the setting the next time you open the diagram. If you want to restore the default behavior, choose **Fit System to View** from the **View** menu the next time you open the diagram.

# Selecting Objects

Many model building actions, such as copying a block or deleting a line, require that you first select one or more blocks and lines (objects).

## Selecting One Object

To select an object, click on it. Small black square "handles" appear at the corners of a selected block and near the end points of a selected line. For example, the figure below shows a selected Sine Wave block and a selected line.

When you select an object by clicking on it, any other selected objects become deselected.

## Selecting More than One Object

You can select more than one object either by selecting objects one at a time, by selecting objects located near each other using a bounding box, or by selecting the entire model.

### Selecting Multiple Objects One at a Time

To select more than one object by selecting each object individually, hold down the **Shift** key and click on each object to be selected. To deselect a selected object, click on the object again while holding down the **Shift** key.

### Selecting Multiple Objects Using a Bounding Box

An easy way to select more than one object in the same area of the window is to draw a bounding box around the objects:

1 Define the starting corner of a bounding box by positioning the pointer at one corner of the box, then pressing and holding down the mouse button. Notice the shape of the cursor.

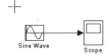

**2** Drag the pointer to the opposite corner of the box. A dotted rectangle encloses the selected blocks and lines.

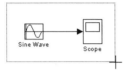

**3** Release the mouse button. All blocks and lines at least partially enclosed by the bounding box are selected.

### Selecting the Entire Model

To select all objects in the active window, choose **Select All** from the **Edit** menu. You cannot create a subsystem by selecting blocks and lines in this way. For more information, see "Creating Subsystems" on page 4–45.

# Blocks

Blocks are the elements from which Simulink models are built. You can model virtually any dynamic system by creating and interconnecting blocks in appropriate ways. This section discusses how to use blocks to build models of dynamic systems.

## Block Data Tips

On Microsoft Windows, Simulink displays information about a block in a pop-up window when you allow the pointer to hover over the block in the diagram view. To disable this feature or control what information a data tip includes, select **Block data tips options** from the Simulink **View** menu.

## Virtual Blocks

When creating models, you need to be aware that Simulink blocks fall into two basic categories: nonvirtual and virtual blocks. Nonvirtual blocks play an active role in the simulation of a system. If you add or remove a nonvirtual block, you change the model's behavior. Virtual blocks, by contrast, play no active role in the simulation; they help organize a model graphically. Some Simulink blocks are virtual in some circumstances and nonvirtual in others. Such blocks are called conditionally virtual blocks. The following table lists Simulink virtual and conditionally virtual blocks.

**Table 4-1: Virtual and Conditionally Virtual Blocks**

| Block Name | Condition Under Which Block Will Be Virtual |
|---|---|
| Bus Selector | Always virtual. |
| Data Store Memory | Always virtual. |
| Demux | Always virtual. |
| Enable Port | Always virtual. |
| From | Always virtual. |
| Goto | Always virtual. |
| Goto Tag Visibility | Always virtual. |

**Table 4-1: Virtual and Conditionally Virtual Blocks (Continued)**

| Block Name | Condition Under Which Block Will Be Virtual |
|---|---|
| Ground | Always virtual. |
| Inport | Virtual *unless* the block resides in a conditionally executed subsystem *and* has a direct connection to an outport block. |
| Mux | Always virtual. |
| Outport | Virtual when the block resides within any subsystem block (conditional or not), and does *not* reside in the root (top-level) Simulink window. |
| Selector | Virtual except in matrix mode. |
| Subsystem | Virtual except if the block is conditionally executed and/or the block's **Treat as Atomic Unit** option is selected. |
| Terminator | Always virtual. |
| Trigger Port | Virtual when the outport port is *not* present. |

## Copying and Moving Blocks from One Window to Another

As you build your model, you often copy blocks from Simulink block libraries or other libraries or models into your model window. To do this, follow these steps:

1 Open the appropriate block library or model window.

2 Drag the block to copy into the target model window. To drag a block, position the cursor over the block icon, then press and hold down the mouse button. Move the cursor into the target window, then release the mouse button.

You can also drag blocks from the Simulink Library Browser into a model window. See "Browsing Block Libraries" on page 4-62 for more information.

**Note** Simulink hides the names of Sum, Mux, Demux, and Bus Selector blocks when you copy them from the Simulink block library to a model. This is done to avoid unnecessarily cluttering the model diagram. (The shapes of these blocks clearly indicate their respective functions.)

You can also copy blocks by using the **Copy** and **Paste** commands from the **Edit** menu:

**1** Select the block you want to copy.

**2** Choose **Copy** from the **Edit** menu.

**3** Make the target model window the active window.

**4** Choose **Paste** from the **Edit** menu.

Simulink assigns a name to each copied block. If it is the first block of its type in the model, its name is the same as its name in the source window. For example, if you copy the Gain block from the Math library into your model window, the name of the new block is Gain. If your model already contains a block named Gain, Simulink adds a sequence number to the block name (for example, Gain1, Gain2). You can rename blocks; see "Manipulating Block Names" on page 4–17.

When you copy a block, the new block inherits all the original block's parameter values.

Simulink uses an invisible five-pixel grid to simplify the alignment of blocks. All blocks within a model snap to a line on the grid. You can move a block slightly up, down, left, or right by selecting the block and pressing the arrow keys.

You can display the grid in the model window by typing the following command in the MATLAB window.

```
set_param('<model name>','showgrid','on')
```

To change the grid spacing, type

```
set_param('<model name>','gridspacing',<number of pixels>)
```

For example, to change the grid spacing to 20 pixels, type

```
set_param('<model name>','gridspacing',20)
```

For either of the above commands, you can also select the model, and then type gcs instead of <model name>.

You can copy or move blocks to compatible applications (such as word processing programs) using the **Copy**, **Cut**, and **Paste** commands. These commands copy only the graphic representation of the blocks, not their parameters.

Moving blocks from one window to another is similar to copying blocks, except that you hold down the **Shift** key while you select the blocks.

You can use the **Undo** command from the **Edit** menu to remove an added block.

## Moving Blocks in a Model

To move a single block from one place to another in a model window, drag the block to a new location. Simulink automatically repositions lines connected to the moved block.

To move more than one block, including connecting lines:

1 Select the blocks and lines. If you need information about how to select more than one block, see "Selecting More than One Object" on page 4–7.

2 Drag the objects to their new location and release the mouse button.

## Copying Blocks in a Model

You can copy blocks in a model as follows. While holding down the **Ctrl** key, select the block with the left mouse button, then drag it to a new location. You can also do this by dragging the block using the right mouse button. Duplicated blocks have the same parameter values as the original blocks. Sequence numbers are added to the new block names.

## Block Parameters

All Simulink blocks have a common set of parameters, called block properties, that you can set (see "Common Block Parameters" in the online Simulink help). See "Block Properties Dialog Box" on page 4-14 for information on setting block properties. In addition, many blocks have one or more block-specific parameters that you can set (see "Block-Specific Parameters" in the online Simulink help). By setting these parameters, you can customize the behavior of the block to meet the specific requirements of your model.

## Setting Block-Specific Parameters

Every block that has block-specific parameters has a dialog box that you can use to view and set the parameters. You can display this dialog by selecting the block in the model window and choosing **BLOCK Parameters** from the model window's **Edit** menu or from the model window's context (right-click) menu, where **BLOCK** is the name of the block you selected, e.g., **Constant Parameters**. You can also display a block's parameter dialog box by double-clicking its icon in the model or library window.

---

**Note** This holds true for all blocks with parameter dialog boxes except for the Subsystem block. You must use the model window's **Edit** menu or context menu to display a Subsystem block's parameter dialog.

---

For information on the parameter dialog of a specific block, see the block's documentation in the block reference in the online Simulink help.

You can set any block parameter, using the Simulink set_param command. See set_param in the online Simulink help for details.

You can use any MATLAB constant, variable, or expression that evaluates to an acceptable result when specifying the value of a parameter in a block parameter dialog or a set_param command.

## Block Properties Dialog Box

This dialog box lets you set a block's properties. To display this dialog, select the block in the model window and then select **BLOCK Properties** from the **Edit** menu, where **BLOCK** is the name of the block you selected, e.g., **Constant**.

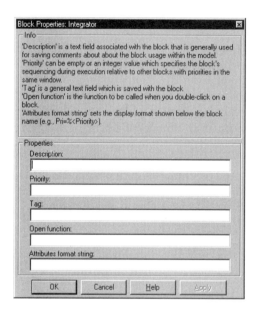

The dialog box contains the following fields.

### Description

Brief description of the block's purpose.

### Priority

Execution priority of this block relative to other blocks in the model. See "Assigning Block Priorities" on page 4-19 for more information.

### Tag

A general text field that is saved with the block.

### Open function

MATLAB (M-) function to be called when a user opens this block.

### Attributes format string

Current value of the block's `AttributesFormatString` parameter. This parameter specifies which parameters to display beneath a block's icon. The "Model and Block Parameters" section in the online Simulink help describes the parameters that a block can have. You can use the AttributesFormatString parameter to display the values of specified parameters beneath the block's icon.

The attributes format string can be any text string that has embedded parameter names. An embedded parameter name is a parameter name preceded by `%<` and followed by `>`, for example, `%<priority>`. Simulink displays the attributes format string beneath the block's icon, replacing each parameter name with the corresponding parameter value. You can use line-feed characters (`\n`) to display each parameter on a separate line. For example, specifying the attributes format string

```
pri=%<priority>\ngain=%<Gain>
```

for a Gain block displays

If a parameter's value is not a string or an integer, Simulink displays `N/S` (not supported) for the parameter's value. If the parameter name is invalid, Simulink displays "???" as the parameter value.

## Deleting Blocks

To delete one or more blocks, select the blocks to be deleted and press the **Delete** or **Backspace** key. You can also choose **Clear** or **Cut** from the **Edit** menu. The **Cut** command writes the blocks into the clipboard, which enables you to paste them into a model. Using the **Delete** or **Backspace** key or the **Clear** command does not enable you to paste the block later.

You can use the **Undo** command from the **Edit** menu to replace a deleted block.

**4-15**

## Changing the Orientation of Blocks

By default, signals flow through a block from left to right. Input ports are on the left, and output ports are on the right. You can change the orientation of a block by choosing one of these commands from the **Format** menu:

- The **Flip Block** command rotates the block 180 degrees.
- The **Rotate Block** command rotates a block clockwise 90 degrees.

The figure below shows how Simulink orders ports after changing the orientation of a block using the **Rotate Block** and **Flip Block** menu items. The text in the blocks shows their orientation.

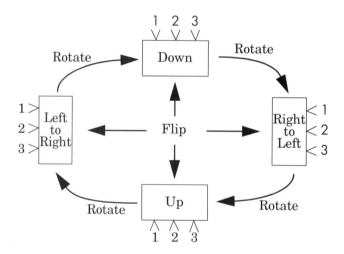

## Resizing Blocks

To change the size of a block, select it, then drag any of its selection handles. While you hold down the mouse button, a dotted rectangle shows the new block size. When you release the mouse button, the block is resized.

For example, the figure below shows a Signal Generator block being resized. The lower-right handle was selected and dragged to the cursor position. When the mouse button is released, the block takes its new size.

This figure shows a block being resized.

## Manipulating Block Names

All block names in a model must be unique and must contain at least one character. By default, block names appear below blocks whose ports are on the sides, and to the left of blocks whose ports are on the top and bottom, as this figure shows.

### Changing Block Names

You can edit a block name in one of these ways:

- To replace the block name on a Microsoft Windows or Linux system, click on the block name, then double-click or drag the cursor to select the entire name. Then, enter the new name.
- To insert characters, click between two characters to position the insertion point, then insert text.
- To replace characters, drag the mouse to select a range of text to replace, then enter the new text.

When you click the pointer someplace else in the model or take any other action, the name is accepted or rejected. If you try to change the name of a block to a name that already exists or to a name with no characters, Simulink displays an error message.

You can modify the font used in a block name by selecting the block, then choosing the **Font** menu item from the **Format** menu. Select a font from the **Set Font** dialog box. This procedure also changes the font of text on the block icon.

You can cancel edits to a block name by choosing **Undo** from the **Edit** menu.

---

**Note** If you change the name of a library block, all links to that block will become unresolved.

---

### Changing the Location of a Block Name

You can change the location of the name of a selected block in two ways:

- By dragging the block name to the opposite side of the block
- By choosing the **Flip Name** command from the **Format** menu. This command changes the location of the block name to the opposite side of the block.

For more information about block orientation, see "Changing the Orientation of Blocks" on page 4–16.

### Changing Whether a Block Name Appears

To change whether the name of a selected block is displayed, choose a menu item from the **Format** menu:

- The **Hide Name** menu item hides a visible block name. When you select **Hide Name**, it changes to **Show Name** when that block is selected.
- The **Show Name** menu item shows a hidden block name.

## Displaying Parameters Beneath a Block's Icon

You can cause Simulink to display one or more of a block's parameters beneath the block's icon in a block diagram. You specify the parameters to be displayed in the following ways:

- By entering an attributes format string in the **Attributes format string** field of the block's **Block Properties** dialog box (see "Block Properties Dialog Box" on page 4-14)
- By setting the value of the block's AttributesFormatString property to the format string, using set_param.

## Disconnecting Blocks

To disconnect a block from its connecting lines, hold down the **Shift** key, then drag the block to a new location.

## Assigning Block Priorities

You can assign execution priorities to nonvirtual blocks in a model. Higher priority blocks execute before lower priority blocks, though not necessarily before blocks that have no assigned priority.

You can assign block priorities interactively or programmatically. To set priorities programmatically, use the command

```
set_param(b,'Priority','n')
```

where b is a block path and n is any valid integer. (Negative numbers and 0 are valid priority values.) The lower the number, the higher the priority; that is, 2 is higher priority than 3. To set a block's priority interactively, enter the priority in the **Priority** field of the block's **Block Properties** dialog box (see "Block Properties Dialog Box" on page 4-14).

Simulink honors the block priorities that you specify only if they are consistent with Simulink's block sorting algorithm (see "Determining Block Update Order" on page 3-10). If the specified priorities are inconsistent, Simulink ignores the specified priority and places the block in an appropriate location in the block execution order. If Simulink is unable to honor a block priority, it displays a Block Priority Violation diagnostic message (see "The Diagnostics Pane" on page 5-24).

## Displaying Block Execution Order

To display the execution order of blocks during simulation, select **Execution order** from the Simulink **Format** menu. Selecting this option causes Simulink to display a number in the top right corner of each block in a block diagram.

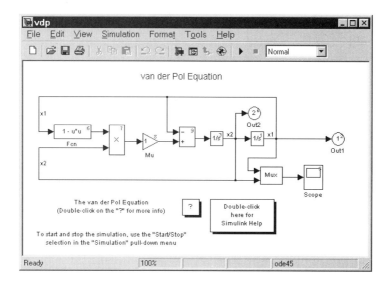

The number indicates the execution order of the block relative to other blocks in the diagram. For example, 1 indicates that the block is the first block executed on every time step, 2 indicates that the block is the second block executed on every time step, and so on.

## Using Drop Shadows

You can add a drop shadow to a block by selecting the block, then choosing **Show Drop Shadow** from the **Format** menu. When you select a block with a drop shadow, the menu item changes to **Hide Drop Shadow**. The figure below shows a Subsystem block with a drop shadow.

## Sample Time Colors

Simulink can color-code the blocks and lines in your model to indicate the sample rates at which the blocks operate.

**Table 4-2: Sample Time Colors**

| Color | Use |
|---|---|
| Black | Continuous blocks |
| Magenta | Constant blocks |
| Yellow | Hybrid (subsystems grouping blocks, or Mux or Demux blocks grouping signals with varying sample times) |
| Red | Fastest discrete sample time |
| Green | Second fastest discrete sample time |
| Blue | Third fastest discrete sample time |
| Light Blue | Fourth fastest discrete sample time |
| Dark Green | Fifth fastest discrete sample time |
| Orange | Sixth fastest discrete sample time |
| Cyan | Blocks in triggered subsystems |
| Gray | Fixed in minor step |

To enable the sample time colors feature, select **Sample Time Colors** from the **Format** menu.

Simulink does not automatically recolor the model with each change you make to it, so you must select **Update Diagram** from the **Edit** menu to explicitly update the model coloration. To return to your original coloring, disable sample time coloration by again choosing **Sample Time Colors**.

When using sample time colors, the color assigned to each block depends on its sample time with respect to other sample times in the model.

It is important to note that Mux and Demux blocks are simply grouping operators – signals passing through them retain their timing information. For this reason, the lines emanating from a Demux block may have different colors if they are driven by sources having different sample times. In this case, the Mux and Demux blocks are color coded as hybrids (yellow) to indicate that they handle signals with multiple rates.

Similarly, Subsystem blocks that contain blocks with differing sample times are also colored as hybrids, because there is no single rate associated with them. If all of the blocks within a subsystem run at a single rate, then the Subsystem block is colored according to that rate.

# Connecting Blocks

You can connect an output port of one block to the input port of another block by drawing a line between the blocks. Lines represent pathways for signals generated by a model to travel among blocks. See "Working with Signals" on page 4–29 for information on signals. The rest of this section explains how to draw lines between blocks.

## Drawing a Line Between Blocks

To connect the output port of one block to the input port of another block:

**1** Position the cursor over the first block's output port. It is not necessary to position the cursor precisely on the port. The cursor shape changes to a cross hair.

**2** Press and hold down the mouse button.

**3** Drag the pointer to the second block's input port. You can position the cursor on or near the port, or in the block. If you position the cursor in the block, the line is connected to the closest input port. The cursor shape changes to a double cross hair.

**4** Release the mouse button. Simulink replaces the port symbols by a connecting line with an arrow showing the direction of the signal flow. You can create lines either from output to input, or from input to output. The arrow is drawn at the appropriate input port, and the signal is the same.

Simulink draws connecting lines using horizontal and vertical line segments. To draw a diagonal line, hold down the **Shift** key while drawing the line.

## Drawing a Branch Line

A *branch line* is a line that starts from an existing line and carries its signal to the input port of a block. Both the existing line and the branch line carry the same signal. Using branch lines enables you to cause one signal to be carried to more than one block.

In this example, the output of the Product block goes to both the Scope block and the To Workspace block.

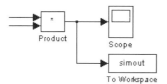

To add a branch line, follow these steps:

**1** Position the pointer on the line where you want the branch line to start.

**2** While holding down the **Ctrl** key, press and hold down the left mouse button.

**3** Drag the pointer to the input port of the target block, then release the mouse button and the **Ctrl** key.

You can also use the right mouse button instead of holding down the left mouse button and the **Ctrl** key.

## Drawing a Line Segment

You may want to draw a line with segments exactly where you want them instead of where Simulink draws them. Or, you might want to draw a line before you copy the block to which the line is connected. You can do either by drawing line segments.

To draw a line segment, you draw a line that ends in an unoccupied area of the diagram. An arrow appears on the unconnected end of the line. To add another line segment, position the cursor over the end of the segment and draw another segment. Simulink draws the segments as horizontal and vertical lines. To draw diagonal line segments, hold down the **Shift** key while you draw the lines.

## Moving a Line Segment

To move a line segment, follow these steps:

**1** Position the pointer on the segment you want to move.

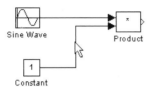

**2** Press and hold down the left mouse button.

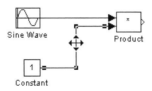

**3** Drag the pointer to the desired location.

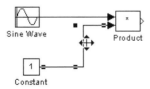

**4** Release the mouse button.

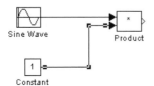

To move the segment connected to an input port, position the pointer over the port and drag the end of the segment to the new location. You cannot move the segment connected to an output port.

## Dividing a Line into Segments

You can divide a line segment into two segments, leaving the ends of the line in their original locations. Simulink creates line segments and a vertex that joins them. To divide a line into segments, follow these steps:

**1** Select the line.

**2** Position the pointer on the line where you want the vertex.

**3** While holding down the **Shift** key, press and hold down the mouse button. The cursor shape changes to a circle that encloses the new vertex.

**4** Drag the pointer to the desired location.

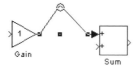

**5** Release the mouse button and the **Shift** key.

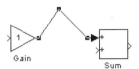

## Moving a Line Vertex

To move a vertex of a line, follow these steps:

**1** Position the pointer on the vertex, then press and hold down the mouse button. The cursor changes to a circle that encloses the vertex.

**2** Drag the pointer to the desired location.

**3** Release the mouse button.

## Inserting Blocks in a Line

You can insert a block in a line by dropping the block on the line. Simulink inserts the block for you at the point where you drop the block. The block that you insert can have only one input and one output.

To insert a block in a line:

**1** Position the pointer over the block and press the left mouse button.

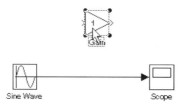

**2** Drag the block over the line in which you want to insert the block.

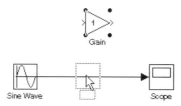

**3** Release the mouse button to drop the block on the line. Simulink inserts the block where you dropped it.

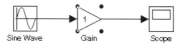

# Working with Signals

This section provides an overview of Simulink signals and explains how to specify, display, and check the validity of signal connections.

## About Signals

Signals are the streams of values that appear at the outputs of Simulink blocks when a model is simulated. It is useful to think of signals as traveling along the lines that connect the blocks in a model diagram. But note that the lines in a Simulink model represent logical, not physical, connections among blocks. Thus, the analogy between Simulink signals and electrical signals is not complete. Electrical signals, for example, take time to cross a wire. The output of a Simulink block, by contrast, appears instantaneously at the input of the block to which it is connected.

### Signal Dimensions

Simulink blocks can output one- or two-dimensional signals. A one-dimensional (1-D) signal consists of a stream of one-dimensional arrays output at a frequency of one array (vector) per simulation time step. A two-dimensional (2-D) signal consists of a stream of two-dimensional arrays emitted at a frequency of one 2-D array (matrix per block sample time. The Simulink user interface and documentation generally refers to 1-D signals as *vectors* and 2-D signals as *matrices*. A one-element array is frequently referred to as a *scalar*. A *row vector* is a 2-D array that has one row. A *column vector* is a 2-D array that has one column.

Simulink blocks vary in the dimensionality of the signals they can accept or output during simulation. Some blocks can accept or output signals of any dimensions. Some can accept or output only scalar or vector signals. To determine the signal dimensionality of a particular block, see the block's description in the "Block Reference" in the online Simulink help. See "Determining Output Signal Dimensions" on page 4-33 for information on what determines the dimensions of output signals for blocks that can output nonscalar signals.

### Complex Signals

The values of Simulink signals can be complex numbers. A signal whose values are complex numbers is called a complex signal. See "Working with Complex

Signals" on page 4-37 for information on creating and manipulating complex signals.

## Virtual Signals

A *virtual signal* is a signal that represents another signal graphically.Virtual blocks, such as a Mux or Subsystem block (see "Virtual Blocks" on page 4-9), generate virtual signals. Like virtual blocks, virtual signals allow you to simplify your model graphically. For example, using a Mux block, you can reduce a large number of nonvirtual signals (i.e., signals originating from nonvirtual blocks) to a single virtual signal, thereby making your model easier to understand. You can think of a virtual signal as a tie-wrap that bundles together a number of signals.

Virtual signals are purely graphical entities. They have no mathematical or physical significance. Simulink ignores them when simulating a model.

Whenever you run or update a model, Simulink determines the nonvirtual signal(s) represented by the model's virtual signal(s), using a procedure known as *signal propagation*. When running the model, Simulink uses the corresponding nonvirtual signal(s), determined via signal propagation, to drive the blocks to which the virtual signals are connected. For example, in the following model,

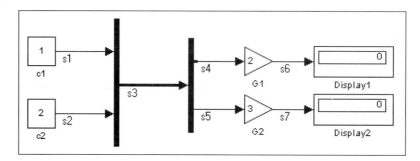

signal s4 appears to drive Gain block G1. However, s4 is a virtual signal. The actual signal driving Gain block G1 is signal s1. Simulink determines this automatically whenever you update or simulate the model.

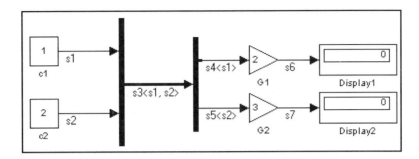

**Note** Virtual signals can represent virtual as well as nonvirtual signals. For example, you can use a Mux block to combine multiple virtual and nonvirtual signals into a single virtual signal. If during signal propagation, Simulink determines that a component of a virtual signal is itself virtual, Simulink determine its nonvirtual component(s), using signal propagation. This process continues until Simulink has determined all nonvirtual components of a virtual signal.

## Signal Buses

You can use Mux and Demux blocks operating in bus selection mode to create signal buses.

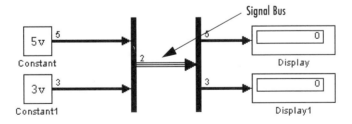

A signal bus is a virtual signal that represents a set of signals. It is analogous to a bundle of wires held together by tie wraps. Simulink uses a special line style to display signal buses. If you select **Signal Dimensions** from Simulink's

Format menu, Simulink displays the number of signal components carried by the bus.

## Signal Glossary

The following table summarizes the terminology used to describe signals in the Simulink user interface and documentation.

| Term | Meaning |
| --- | --- |
| Complex signal | Signal whose values are complex numbers |
| Data type | Format used to represent signal values internally. |
| Matrix | Two-dimensional signal array |
| Real signal | Signal whose values are real (as opposed to complex) numbers |
| Scalar | One-element array, i.e., a one-element, 1-D or 2-D array |
| Signal bus | Signal created by a Mux or Demux block. |
| Signal propagation | Process used by Simulink to determine attributes of signals and blocks, such as data types, labels, sample time, dimensionality, and so on, that are determined by connectivity |
| Size | Number of elements that a signal contains. The size of a matrix (2-D) signal is generally expressed as M-by-N where M is the number of columns and N is the number of rows making up the signal. |
| Vector | One-dimensional signal array |
| Width | Size of a vector signal |
| Virtual signal | Signal that represents another signal or set of signals. |

## Determining Output Signal Dimensions

If a block can emit nonscalar signals, the dimensions of the signals that the block outputs depends on the block's parameters, if the block is a source block; otherwise, the output dimensions depend on the dimensions of the block's input and parameters.

### Determining the Output Dimensions of Source Blocks

A *source* block is a block that has no inputs. Examples of source blocks include the Constant block and the Sine Wave block. (See the "Sources Library Blocks" table in the "Block Reference" in the online Simulink help for a complete listing of Simulink source blocks.) The output dimensions of a source block are the same as that of its output value parameter(s) if the block's **Interpret Vector Parameters as 1-D** parameter is off (i.e., not checked in the block's parameter dialog box). If the **Interpret Vector Parameters as 1-D** parameter is on, the output dimensions equal the output value parameter dimensions except if the parameter dimensions are N-by-1 or 1-by-N. In the latter case, the block outputs a vector signal of width N.

As an example of how a source block's output value parameter(s) and **Interpret Vector Parameters as 1-D** parameter determine the dimensionality of its output, consider the Constant block. This block outputs a constant signal equal to its **Constant value** parameter. The following table illustrates how the dimensionality of the **Constant value** parameter and the setting of the **Interpret Vector Parameters as 1-D** parameter determine the dimensionality of the block's output.

| Constant Value | Interpret Vector Parameters as 1-D | Output |
| --- | --- | --- |
| 2-D scalar | off | 2-D scalar |
| 2-D scalar | on | 1-D scalar |
| 1-by-N matrix | off | 1-by-N matrix |
| 1-by-N matrix | on | N-element vector |
| N-by-1 matrix | off | N-by-1 matrix |
| N-by-1 matrix | on | N-element vector |

| Constant Value | Interpret Vector Parameters as 1-D | Output |
|---|---|---|
| M-by-N matrix | off | M-by-N matrix |
| M-by-N matrix | on | M-by-N matrix |

Simulink source blocks allow you to specify the dimensions of the signals that they output. You can therefore use them to introduce signals of various dimensions into your model.

### Determining the Output Dimensions of Non-Source Blocks

If a block has inputs, the dimensions of its outputs are, after scalar expansion, the same as those of its inputs. (All inputs must have the same dimensions as discussed in the next section.)

## Signal and Parameter Dimension Rules

When creating a Simulink model, you must observe the following rules regarding signal and parameter dimensions.

### Input Signal Dimension Rule

All nonscalar inputs to a block must have the same dimensions.

A block may have a mix of scalar and nonscalar inputs as long as all the nonscalar inputs have the same dimensions. Simulink expands the scalar inputs to have the same dimensions as the nonscalar inputs (see "Scalar Expansion of Inputs" on page 4-35), thus preserving the general rule.

### Block Parameter Dimension Rule

In general, a block's parameters must have the same dimensions as the corresponding inputs.

Two seeming exceptions exist to this general rule:

- A block may have scalar parameters corresponding to nonscalar inputs. In this case, Simulink expands a scalar parameter to have the same dimensions as the corresponding input (see "Scalar Expansion of Parameters" on page 4-36), thus preserving the general rule.

- If an input is a vector, the corresponding parameter may be either an N-by-1 or a 1-by-N matrix. In this case, Simulink applies the N matrix elements to the corresponding elements of the input vector. This exception allows use of MATLAB row or column vectors, which are actually 1-by-N or N-by-1 matrices, respectively, to specify parameters that apply to vector inputs.

### Vector or Matrix Input Conversion Rules

Simulink converts vectors to row or column matrices and row or column matrices to vectors under the following circumstances:

- If a vector signal is connected to an input that requires a matrix, Simulink converts the vector to a one-row or one-column matrix.
- If a one-column or one-row matrix is connected to an input that requires a vector, Simulink converts the matrix to a vector.
- If the inputs to a block consist of a mixture of vectors and matrices and the matrix inputs all have one column or one row, Simulink converts the vectors to matrices having one column or one row, respectively.

---

**Note** You can configure Simulink to display a warning or error message if a vector or matrix conversion occurs during a simulation. See "Configuration options" on page 5–25 for more information.

---

## Scalar Expansion of Inputs and Parameters

*Scalar expansion* is the conversion of a scalar value into a nonscalar array of the same dimensions. Many Simulink blocks support scalar expansion of inputs and parameters. Block descriptions in the "Block Reference" in the online Simulink help indicate whether Simulink applies scalar expansion to a block's inputs and parameters.

### Scalar Expansion of Inputs

Scalar expansion of inputs refers to the expansion of scalar inputs to match the dimensions of other nonscalar inputs or nonscalar parameters.When the input to a block is a mix of scalar and nonscalar signals, Simulink expands the scalar inputs into nonscalar signals having the same dimensions as the other nonscalar inputs. The elements of an expanded signal equal the value of the scalar from which the signal was expanded.

The following model illustrates scalar expansion of inputs. This model adds scalar and vector inputs. The input from block Constant1 is scalar expanded to match the size of the vector input from the Constant block. The input is expanded to the vector [3 3 3].

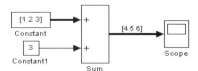

When a block's output is a function of a parameter and the parameter is nonscalar, Simulink expands a scalar input to match the dimensions of the parameter. For example, Simulink expands a scalar input to a Gain block to match the dimensions of a nonscalar gain parameter.

### Scalar Expansion of Parameters

If a block has a nonscalar input and a corresponding parameter is a scalar, Simulink expands the scalar parameter to have the same number of elements as the input. Each element of the expanded parameter equals the value of the original scalar. Simulink then applies each element of the expanded parameter to the corresponding input element.

This example shows that a scalar parameter (the Gain) is expanded to a vector of identically valued elements to match the size of the block input, a three-element vector.

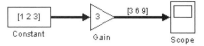

## Working with Complex Signals

By default, the values of Simulink signals are real numbers. However, models can create and manipulates signals that have complex numbers as values.

You can introduce a complex-valued signal into a model in the following ways:

- Load complex-valued signal data from the MATLAB workspace into the model via a root-level inport.
- Create a Constant block in your model and set its value to a complex number.
- Create real signals corresponding to the real and imaginary parts of a complex signal and then combine the parts into a complex signal, using Real-Imag to Complex conversion block.

You can manipulate complex signals via blocks that accept them. If you are not sure whether a block accepts complex signals, see the documentation for the block in the "Block Reference" section of the Simulink online documentation.

## Checking Signal Connections

Many Simulink blocks have limitations on the types of signals they can accept. Before simulating a model, Simulink checks all of blocks to ensure that they can accommodate the types of signals output by the ports to which they are connected. If any incompatibilities exist, Simulink reports an error and terminates the simulation. To detect such errors before running a simulation, choose **Update Diagram** from the Simulink **Edit** menu. Simulink reports any invalid connections found in the process of updating the diagram.

## Setting Signal Display Options

Simulink offers the following options for displaying signal attributes.

| Signal Display Option | Description |
| --- | --- |
| **Wide nonscalar lines** | Draws lines that carry vector or matrix signal wider than lines that carry scalar signals. |
| **Signal dimensions** | Displays the dimensions of a signal next to the line that carries it. |
| **Port data types** | Displays the data type and signal type of a signal next to the output port that emits the signal. |

You can set these options via either Simulink's **Format** menu or its model context (right-click) menu.

## Signal Names

You can assign names to signals by:

- Editing the signal's label
- Setting the name parameter of the port or line that represents the signal, e.g.,

```
p = get_param(gcb, 'PortHandles')
l = get_param(p.Inport, 'Line')
set_param(l, 'Name', 's9')
```

## Signal Labels

A signal's label displays the signal's name. A virtual signal's label optionally displays the signals it represents in angle brackets. You can edit a signal's label, thereby changing the signal's name.

To create a signal label (and thereby name the signal), double-click on the line that represents the signal. The text cursor appears. Type the name and click anywhere outside the label to exit label editing mode.

---

**Note** When you create a signal label, take care to double-click *on* the line. If you click in an unoccupied area close to the line, you will create a model annotation instead.

---

Labels can appear above or below horizontal lines or line segments, and left or right of vertical lines or line segments. Labels can appear at either end, at the center, or in any combination of these locations.

To move a signal label, drag the label to a new location on the line. When you release the mouse button, the label fixes its position near the line.

To copy a signal label, hold down the **Ctrl** key while dragging the label to another location on the line. When you release the mouse button, the label appears in both the original and the new locations.

To edit an existing signal label, select it:

• To replace the label, click on the label, then double-click or drag the cursor to select the entire label. Then, enter the new label.

• To insert characters, click between two characters to position the insertion point, then insert text.

• To replace characters, drag the mouse to select a range of text to replace, then enter the new text.

To delete all occurrences of a signal label, delete all the characters in the label. When you click outside the label, the labels are deleted. To delete a single occurrence of the label, hold down the **Shift** key while you select the label, then press the **Delete** or **Backspace** key.

To change the font of a signal label, select the signal, choose **Font** from the **Format** menu, then select a font from the **Set Font** dialog box.

## Displaying Signals Represented by Virtual Signals

To display the signal(s) represented by a virtual signal, click the signal's label and enter an angle bracket (<) after the signal's name. (If the signal has no name, simply enter the angle bracket.) Click anywhere outside the signal's label. Simulink exits label editing mode and displays the signals represented by the virtual signal in brackets in the label.

# Annotations

Annotations provide textual information about a model. You can add an annotation to any unoccupied area of your block diagram.

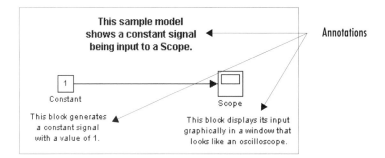

To create a model annotation, double-click on an unoccupied area of the block diagram. A small rectangle appears and the cursor changes to an insertion point. Start typing the annotation contents. Each line is centered within the rectangle that surrounds the annotation.

To move an annotation, drag it to a new location.

To edit an annotation, select it:

- To replace the annotation on a Microsoft Windows or Linux system, click on the annotation, then double-click or drag the cursor to select it. Then, enter the new annotation.

- To insert characters, click between two characters to position the insertion point, then insert text.

- To replace characters, drag the mouse to select a range of text to replace, then enter the new text.

To delete an annotation, hold down the **Shift** key while you select the annotation, then press the **Delete** or **Backspace** key.

To change the font of all or part of an annotation, select the text in the annotation you want to change, then choose **Font** from the **Format** menu. Select a font and size from the dialog box.

To change the text alignment (e.g., left, center, or right) of the annotation, select the annotation and choose **Text Alignment** from the model window's

**Format** or context menu. Then choose one of the alignment options (e.g., **Center**) from the **Text Alignment** submenu.

# Summary of Mouse and Keyboard Actions

These tables summarize the use of the mouse and keyboard to manipulate blocks, lines, and signal labels. LMB means press the left mouse button; CMB, the center mouse button; and RMB, the right mouse button.

The first table lists mouse and keyboard actions that apply to blocks.

**Table 4-3: Manipulating Blocks**

| Task | Microsoft Windows | Linux |
|------|-------------------|-------|
| Select one block | LMB | LMB |
| Select multiple blocks | **Shift** + LMB | **Shift** + LMB; or CMB alone |
| Select next block | **Tab** | **Tab** |
| Select previous block | **Shift** + **Tab** | **Shift** + **Tab** |
| Copy block from another window | Drag block | Drag block |
| Move block | Drag block | Drag block |
| Duplicate block | **Ctrl** + LMB and drag; or RMB and drag | **Ctrl** + LMB and drag; or RMB and drag |
| Connect blocks | LMB | LMB |
| Disconnect block | **Shift** + drag block | **Shift** + drag block; or CMB and drag |
| Open selected subsystem | **Enter** | **Return** |
| Go to parent of selected subsystem | **Esc** | **Esc** |

The next table lists mouse and keyboard actions that apply to lines.

**Table 4-4: Manipulating Lines**

| Task | Microsoft Windows | Linux |
|---|---|---|
| Select one line | LMB | LMB |
| Select multiple lines | **Shift** + LMB | **Shift** + LMB; or CMB alone |
| Draw branch line | **Ctrl** + drag line; or **RMB** and drag line | **Ctrl** + drag line; or RMB + drag line |
| Route lines around blocks | **Shift** + draw line segments | **Shift** + draw line segments; or CMB and draw segments |
| Move line segment | Drag segment | Drag segment |
| Move vertex | Drag vertex | Drag vertex |
| Create line segments | **Shift** + drag line | **Shift** + drag line; or CMB + drag line |

The next table lists mouse and keyboard actions that apply to signal labels.

**Table 4-5: Manipulating Signal Labels**

| Action | Microsoft Windows | Linux |
|---|---|---|
| Create signal label | Double-click on line, then type label | Double-click on line, then type label |
| Copy signal label | **Ctrl** + drag label | **Ctrl** + drag label |
| Move signal label | Drag label | Drag label |
| Edit signal label | Click in label, then edit | Click in label, then edit |
| Delete signal label | **Shift** + click on label, then press **Delete** | **Shift** + click on label, then press **Delete** |

The next table lists mouse and keyboard actions that apply to annotations.

**Table 4-6: Manipulating Annotations**

| Action | Microsoft Windows | Linux |
| --- | --- | --- |
| Create annotation | Double-click in diagram, then type text | Double-click in diagram, then type text |
| Copy annotation | **Ctrl** + drag label | **Ctrl** + drag label |
| Move annotation | Drag label | Drag label |
| Edit annotation | Click in text, then edit | Click in text, then edit |
| Delete annotation | **Shift** + select annotation, then press **Delete** | **Shift** + select annotation, then press **Delete** |

# Creating Subsystems

As your model increases in size and complexity, you can simplify it by grouping blocks into subsystems. Using subsystems has these advantages:

- It helps reduce the number of blocks displayed in your model window.
- It allows you to keep functionally related blocks together.
- It enables you to establish a hierarchical block diagram, where a Subsystem block is on one layer and the blocks that make up the subsystem are on another.

You can create a subsystem in two ways:

- Add a Subsystem block to your model, then open that block and add the blocks it contains to the subsystem window.
- Add the blocks that make up the subsystem, then group those blocks into a subsystem.

## Creating a Subsystem by Adding the Subsystem Block

To create a subsystem before adding the blocks it contains, add a Subsystem block to the model, then add the blocks that make up the subsystem:

**1** Copy the Subsystem block from the Signals & Systems library into your model.

**2** Open the Subsystem block by double-clicking on it.

Simulink opens the subsystem in the current or a new model window, depending on the model window reuse mode that you have selected (see "Window Reuse" on page 4-48).

**3** In the empty Subsystem window, create the subsystem. Use Inport blocks to represent input from outside the subsystem and Outport blocks to represent external output.

For example, the subsystem below includes a Sum block and Inport and Outport blocks to represent input to and output from the subsystem:

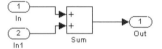

## Creating a Subsystem by Grouping Existing Blocks

If your model already contains the blocks you want to convert to a subsystem, you can create the subsystem by grouping those blocks:

**1** Enclose the blocks and connecting lines that you want to include in the subsystem within a bounding box. You cannot specify the blocks to be grouped by selecting them individually or by using the **Select All** command. For more information, see "Selecting Multiple Objects Using a Bounding Box" on page 4–7.

For example, this figure shows a model that represents a counter. The Sum and Unit Delay blocks are selected within a bounding box.

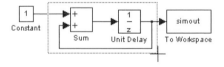

When you release the mouse button, the two blocks and all the connecting lines are selected.

**2** Choose **Create Subsystem** from the **Edit** menu. Simulink replaces the selected blocks with a Subsystem block.

This figure shows the model after choosing the **Create Subsystem** command (and resizing the Subsystem block so the port labels are readable).

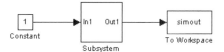

If you open the Subsystem block, Simulink displays the underlying system, as shown below. Notice that Simulink adds Inport and Outport blocks to represent input from and output to blocks outside the subsystem.

As with all blocks, you can change the name of the Subsystem block. Also, you can customize the icon and dialog box for the block using the masking feature, described in Chapter 7, "Using Masks to Customize Blocks."

## Model Navigation Commands

Subsystems allow you to create a hierarchical model comprising many layers. You can navigate this hierarchy, using the Simulink Model Browser (see "Searching and Browsing Models" on page 4-75) and/or the following model navigation commands.

- **Open**

  The **Open** command opens the currently selected subsystem. To execute the command, choose **Open** from the Simulink **Edit** menu, type Enter, or double-click the subsystem.

- **Go to Parent**

  The **Go to Parent** command displays the parent of the subsystem displayed in the current window. To execute the command, type Esc or select **Go to Parent** from the Simulink **View** menu.

# Window Reuse

You can specify whether Simulink's model navigation commands use the current window or a new window to display a subsystem or its parent. Reusing windows avoids cluttering your screen with windows. Creating a window for each subsystem allows you to view subsystems side-by-side with their parents or siblings. To specify your preference regarding window reuse, select **Preferences** from the Simulink **File** menu and then select one of the following **Window reuse type** options listed in the Simulink **Preferences** dialog box.

| Reuse Type | Open Action | Go to Parent (Esc) Action |
|---|---|---|
| none | Subsystem appears in a new window. | Parent window moves to the front. |
| reuse | Subsystem replaces the parent in the current window. | Parent window replaces subsystem in current window |
| replace | Subsystem appears in a new window. Parent window disappears. | Parent window appears. Subsystem window disappears. |
| mixed | Subsystem appears in its own window. | Parent window rises to front. Subsystem window disappears. |

# Labeling Subsystem Ports

Simulink labels ports on a Subsystem block. The labels are the names of Inport and Outport blocks that connect the subsystem to blocks outside the subsystem through these ports.

You can hide (or show) the port labels by:

- Selecting the Subsystem block, then choosing **Hide Port Labels** (or **Show Port Labels**) from the **Format** menu
- Selecting an Inport or Outport block in the subsystem and choosing **Hide Name** (or **Show Name**) from the **Format** menu
- Checking the **Show port labels** option in the Subsystem block's parameter dialog

This figure shows two models. The subsystem on the left contains two Inport blocks and one Outport block. The Subsystem block on the right shows the labeled ports.

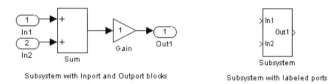

Subsystem with Inport and Outport blocks                Subsystem with labeled ports

## Controlling Access to Subsystems

Simulink allows you to control user access to subsystems that reside in libraries. In particular, you can prevent a user from viewing or modifying the contents of a library subsystem while still allowing the user to employ the subsystem in a model.

To control access to a library subsystem, open the subsystem's parameter dialog box and set its `Access` parameter to either `ReadOnly` or `NoReadOrWrite`. The first option allows a user to view the contents of the library subsystem and make local copies but prevents the user from modifying the original library copy. The second option prevents the user from viewing the contents of, creating local copies, or modifying the permissions of the library subsystem. See the Subsystem block for more information on subsystem access options. Note that both options allow a user to use the library system in models by creating links (see "Libraries" on page 4-57).

# Using Callback Routines

You can define MATLAB expressions that execute when the block diagram or a block is acted upon in a particular way. These expressions, called *callback routines*, are associated with block or model parameters. For example, the callback associated with a block's OpenFcn parameter is executed when the model user double-clicks on that block's name or path changes.

To define callback routines and associate them with parameters, use the set_param command (see set_param in the "Model Construction Commands section of the Simulink online help).

For example, this command evaluates the variable testvar when the user double-clicks on the Test block in mymodel.

```
set_param('mymodel/Test', 'OpenFcn', testvar)
```

You can examine the clutch system (clutch.mdl) for routines associated with many model callbacks.

## Tracing Callbacks

Callback tracing allows you to determine which callbacks Simulink invokes and in what order Simulink invokes them when you open or simulate a model. To enable callback tracking, select the **Callback tracing** option on the Simulink Preferences dialog box (see "Setting Simulink Preferences" on page 2-16) or execute set_param(0, 'CallbackTracing', 'on'). This options causes Simulink to list callbacks in the MATLAB command window as they are invoked.

## Model Callback Parameters

This table lists the parameters for which you can define model callback routines, and indicate when those callback routines are executed. Routines that are executed before or after actions take place occur immediately before or after the action.

| Parameter | When Executed |
|-----------|---------------|
| CloseFcn | Before the block diagram is closed. |
| PostLoadFcn | After the model is loaded. Defining a callback routine for this parameter might be useful for generating an interface that requires that the model has already been loaded. |
| InitFcn | Called at start of model simulation. |
| PostSaveFcn | After the model is saved. |
| PreLoadFcn | Before the model is loaded. Defining a callback routine for this parameter might be useful for loading variables used by the model. |
| PreSaveFcn | Before the model is saved. |
| StartFcn | Before the simulation starts. |
| StopFcn | After the simulation stops. Output is written to workspace variables and files before the StopFcn is executed. |

## Block Callback Parameters

This table lists the parameters for which you can define block callback routines, and indicate when those callback routines are executed. Routines that are executed before or after actions take place occur immediately before or after the action.

| Parameter | When Executed |
| --- | --- |
| CloseFcn | When the block is closed using the close_system command. |
| CopyFcn | After a block is copied. The callback is recursive for Subsystem blocks (that is, if you copy a Subsystem block that contains a block for which the CopyFcn parameter is defined, the routine is also executed). The routine is also executed if an add_block command is used to copy the block. |
| DeleteFcn | Before a block is deleted. This callback is recursive for Subsystem blocks. |
| DestroyFcn | When block has been destroyed. |
| InitFcn | Before the block diagram is compiled and before block parameters are evaluated. |
| LoadFcn | After the block diagram is loaded. This callback is recursive for Subsystem blocks. |
| ModelCloseFcn | Before the block diagram is closed. This callback is recursive for Subsystem blocks. |
| MoveFcn | When block is moved or resized. |
| NameChangeFcn | After a block's name and/or path changes. When a Subsystem block's path is changed, it recursively calls this function for all blocks it contains after calling its own NameChangeFcn routine. |

| Parameter | When Executed |
|-----------|---------------|
| OpenFcn | When the block is opened. This parameter is generally used with Subsystem blocks. The routine is executed when you double-click on the block or when an open_system command is called with the block as an argument. The OpenFcn parameter overrides the normal behavior associated with opening a block, which is to display the block's dialog box or to open the subsystem. |
| ParentCloseFcn | Before closing a subsystem containing the block or when the block is made part of a new subsystem using the new_system command (see new_system in the Simulink online help for more information). |
| PreSaveFcn | Before the block diagram is saved. This callback is recursive for Subsystem blocks. |
| PostSaveFcn | After the block diagram is saved. This callback is recursive for Subsystem blocks. |
| StartFcn | After the block diagram is compiled and before the simulation starts. In the case of an S-Function block, StartFcn executes immediately before the first execution of the block's mdlProcessParameters function. See "S-Function Callback Methods" in *Writing S-Functions* in the Simulink online help for more information. |
| StopFcn | At any termination of the simulation. In the case of an S-Function block, StopFcn executes after the block's mdlTerminate function executes. See "S-Function Callback Methods" in *Writing S-Functions* in the Simulink online help for more information. |
| UndoDeleteFcn | When a block delete is undone. |

| Parameter | When Executed |
|---|---|
| CloseFcn | When the block is closed using the close_system command. |
| CopyFcn | After a block is copied. The callback is recursive for Subsystem blocks (that is, if you copy a Subsystem block that contains a block for which the CopyFcn parameter is defined, the routine is also executed). The routine is also executed if an add_block command is used to copy the block. |
| DeleteFcn | Before a block is deleted. This callback is recursive for Subsystem blocks. |
| DestroyFcn | When block has been destroyed. |
| InitFcn | Before the block diagram is compiled and before block parameters are evaluated. |
| LoadFcn | After the block diagram is loaded. This callback is recursive for Subsystem blocks. |
| ModelCloseFcn | Before the block diagram is closed. This callback is recursive for Subsystem blocks. |
| MoveFcn | When block is moved or resized. |
| NameChangeFcn | After a block's name and/or path changes. When a Subsystem block's path is changed, it recursively calls this function for all blocks it contains after calling its own NameChangeFcn routine. |

| Parameter | When Executed |
|---|---|
| OpenFcn | When the block is opened. This parameter is generally used with Subsystem blocks. The routine is executed when you double-click on the block or when an open_system command is called with the block as an argument. The OpenFcn parameter overrides the normal behavior associated with opening a block, which is to display the block's dialog box or to open the subsystem. |
| ParentCloseFcn | Before closing a subsystem containing the block or when the block is made part of a new subsystem using the new_system command (see new_system in the "Model Creation Commands" section of the Simulink online help). |
| PreSaveFcn | Before the block diagram is saved. This callback is recursive for Subsystem blocks. |
| PostSaveFcn | After the block diagram is saved. This callback is recursive for Subsystem blocks. |
| StartFcn | After the block diagram is compiled and before the simulation starts. In the case of an S-Function block, StartFcn executes immediately before the first execution of the block's mdlProcessParameters function. See "S-Function Callback Methods" in Writing S-Functions in the Simulink online help for more information. |
| StopFcn | At any termination of the simulation. In the case of an S-Function block, StopFcn executes after the block's mdlTerminate function executes. See "S-Function Callback Methods" in Writing S-Functions in the Simulink online help for more information. |
| UndoDeleteFcn | When a block delete is undone. |

# Tips for Building Models

Here are some model-building hints you might find useful:

- Memory issues

  In general, the more memory, the better Simulink performs.

- Using hierarchy

  More complex models often benefit from adding the hierarchy of subsystems to the model. Grouping blocks simplifies the top level of the model and can make it easier to read and understand the model. For more information, see "Creating Subsystems" on page 4–45. The Model Browser (see "The Model Browser" on page 4-81) provides useful information about complex models.

- Cleaning up models

  Well organized and documented models are easier to read and understand. Signal labels and model annotations can help describe what is happening in a model. For more information, see "Signal Names" on page 4–38 and "Drawing a Line Between Blocks" on page 4–23.

- Modeling strategies

  If several of your models tend to use the same blocks, you might find it easier to save these blocks in a model. Then, when you build new models, just open this model and copy the commonly used blocks from it. You can create a block library by placing a collection of blocks into a system and saving the system. You can then access the system by typing its name in the MATLAB command window.

  Generally, when building a model, design it first on paper, then build it using the computer. Then, when you start putting the blocks together into a model, add the blocks to the model window before adding the lines that connect them. This way, you can reduce how often you need to open block libraries.

# Libraries

Libraries enable users to copy blocks into their models from external libraries and automatically update the copied blocks when the source blocks change. Using libraries allows users who develop their own block libraries, or who use those provided by others (such as blocksets), to ensure that their models automatically include the most recent versions of these blocks.

## Terminology

It is important to understand the terminology used with this feature.

*Library* – A collection of library blocks. A library must be explicitly created using **New Library** from the **File** menu.

*Library block* – A block in a library.

*Reference block* – A copy of a library block.

*Link* – The connection between the reference block and its library block that allows Simulink to update the reference block when the library block changes.

*Copy* – The operation that creates a reference block from either a library block or another reference block.

This figure illustrates this terminology.

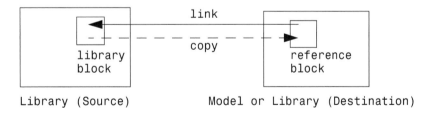

Library (Source)          Model or Library (Destination)

## Creating a Library Link

To create a link to a library block in a model, copy the block's icon from the library to the model (see "Copying and Moving Blocks from One Window to Another" on page 4-10) or by dragging the block from the Library Browser (see "Browsing Block Libraries" on page 4-62) into the model window.

When you copy a library block into a model or another library, Simulink creates a link to the library block. The reference block is a copy of the library block. You can change the values of the reference block's parameters but you cannot mask the block or, if it is masked, edit the mask. Also, you cannot set callback parameters for a reference block. If the link is to a subsystem, you can modify the contents of the reference subsystem (see "Modifying a Linked Subsystem" on page 4-59).

The library and reference blocks are linked *by name*; that is, the reference block is linked to the specific block and library whose names are in effect at the time the copy is made.

If Simulink is unable to find either the library block or the source library on your MATLAB path when it attempts to update the reference block, the link becomes *unresolved*. Simulink issues an error message and displays these blocks using red dashed lines. The error message is

```
Failed to find block "source-block-name"
in library "source-library-name"
referenced by block
"reference-block-path".
```

The unresolved reference block is displayed like this (colored red).

To fix a bad link, you must either:

- Delete the unlinked reference block and copy the library block back into your model.
- Add the directory that contains the required library to the MATLAB path and select **Update Diagram** from the **Edit** menu.
- Double-click on the reference block. On the dialog box that appears, correct the pathname and click on **Apply** or **Close**.

## Disabling Library Links

Simulink allows you to disable linked blocks in a model. Simulink ignores disabled links when simulating a model. To disable a link, select the link, choose **Link options** from the model window's **Edit** or context menu, then choose **Disable link**. To restore a disabled link, choose **Restore link** from the **Link Options** menu.

## Modifying a Linked Subsystem

Simulink allows you to modify subsystems that are library links. If your modifications alter the structure of the subsystem, you must disable the link from the reference block to the library block. If you attempt to modify the structure of a subsystem link, Simulink prompts you to disable the link. Examples of structural modifications include adding or deleting a block or line or change the number of ports on a block. Examples of nonstructural changes include changes to parameter values that do not affect the structure of the subsystem.

## Propagating Link Modifications

Simulink allows a model to have active links with nonstructural but not structural changes. If you restore a link that has structural changes, Simulink prompts you to either propagate or discard the changes. If you choose to propagate the changes, Simulink updates the library block with the changes made in the reference block. If you choose to discard the changes, Simulink replaces the modified reference block with the original library block. In either case, the end result is that the reference block is an exact copy of the library block.

If you restore a link with nonstructural changes, Simulink enables the link without prompting you to propagate or discard the changes. If you want to propagate or discard the changes at a later time, select the reference block, choose **Link options** from the model window's **Edit** or context menu, then choose **Propagate/Discard changes**. If you want to view the nonstructural parameter differences between a reference block and its corresponding library block, choose **View changes** from the **Link options** menu.

## Updating a Linked Block

Simulink updates out-of-date reference blocks in a model or library at these times:

• When the model or library is loaded

• When you select **Update Diagram** from the **Edit** menu or run the simulation

- When you query the LinkStatus parameter of a block using the get_param command (see "Library Link Status" on page 4-61)
- When you use the find_system command

## Breaking a Link to a Library Block

You can break the link between a reference block and its library block to cause the reference block to become a simple copy of the library block, unlinked to the library block. Changes to the library block no longer affect the block. Breaking links to library blocks enables you to transport a model as a stand-alone model, without the libraries.

To break the link between a reference block and its library block, first disable the block. Then select the block and choose **Break Library Link** from the **Link options** menu. You can also break the link between a reference block and its library block from the command line by changing the value of the LinkStatus parameter to 'none' using this command.

```
set_param('refblock', 'LinkStatus', 'none')
```

You can save a system and break all links between reference blocks and library blocks using this command.

```
save_system('sys', 'newname', 'BreakLinks')
```

## Finding the Library Block for a Reference Block

To find the source library and block linked to a reference block, select the reference block, then choose **Go To Library Link** from the **Link options** submenu of the model window's **Edit** or context menu. If the library is open, Simulink selects the library block (displaying selection handles on the block) and makes the source library the active window. If the library is not open, Simulink opens it and selects the library block.

## Library Link Status

All blocks have a `LinkStatus` parameter that indicates whether the block is a reference block. The parameter can have these values.

| Status | Description |
| --- | --- |
| none | Block is not a reference block. |
| resolved | Link is resolved. |
| unresolved | Link is unresolved. |
| implicit | Block is within a linked block. |
| inactive | Link is disabled. |

## Displaying Library Links

Simulink optionally displays an arrow in the bottom left corner of each icon that represents a library link in a model.

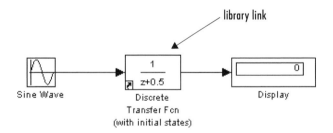

This arrow allows you to tell at a glance whether an icon represents a link to a library block or a local instance of a block. To enable display of library links, select **Library Link Display** from the model window's **Format** menu and then select either **User** (displays only links to user libraries) or **All** (displays all links).

The color of the link arrow indicates the status of the link.

| Color | Status |
|-------|--------|
| Black | Active link |
| Grey | Inactive link |
| Red | Active and modified |

## Getting Information About Library Blocks

Use the `libinfo` command to get information about reference blocks in a system. The format for the command is

```
libdata = libinfo(sys)
```

where sys is the name of the system. The command returns a structure of size n-by-1, where n is the number of library blocks in sys. Each element of the structure has four fields:

- `Block`, the block path
- `Library`, the library name
- `ReferenceBlock`, the reference block path
- `LinkStatus`, the link status, either `'resolved'` or `'unresolved'`

## Browsing Block Libraries

The Library Browser lets you quickly locate and copy library blocks into a model. To display the Library Browser, click the **Library Browser** button in the toolbar of the MATLAB desktop or Simulink model window or type `simulink` at the MATLAB command line.

---

**Note** The Library Browser is available only on Microsoft Windows platforms.

---

The Library Browser contains three panes.

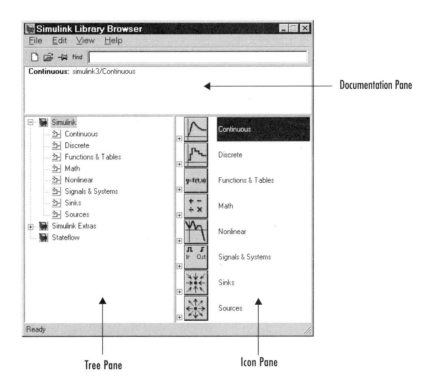

Documentation Pane

Tree Pane

Icon Pane

The tree pane displays all the block libraries installed on your system. The icon pane displays the icons of the blocks that reside in the library currently selected in the tree pane. The documentation pane displays documentation for the block selected in the icon pane.

You can locate blocks either by navigating the Library Browser's library tree or by using the Library Browser's search facility.

### Navigating the Library Tree

The library tree displays a list of all the block libraries installed on the system. You can view or hide the contents of libraries by expanding or collapsing the tree using the mouse or keyboard. To expand/collapse the tree, click the +/- buttons next to library entries or select an entry and press the +/- or right/left arrow key on your keyboard. Use the up/down arrow keys to move up or down the tree.

### Searching Libraries

To find a particular block, enter the block's name in the edit field next to the Library Browser's **Find** button and then click the **Find** button.

### Opening a Library

To open a library, right-click the library's entry in the browser. Simulink displays an **Open Library** button. Select the **Open Library** button to open the library.

### Creating and Opening Models

To create a model, select the **New** button on the Library Browser's toolbar. To open an existing model, select the **Open** button on the toolbar.

### Copying Blocks

To copy a block from the Library Browser into a model, select the block in the browser, drag the selected block into the model window, and drop it where you want to create the copy.

### Displaying Help on a Block

To display help on a block, right-click the block in the Library Browser and select the button that subsequently pops up.

### Pinning the Library Browser

To keep the Library Browser above all other windows on your desktop, select the **PushPin** button on the browser's toolbar.

## Adding Libraries to the Library Browser

If you want a library that you have created to appear in the Library Browser, you must create an slblocks.m file that describes the library in the directory that contains it. The easiest way to create an slblocks.m file is to use an existing slblocks.m file as a template. You can find all existing slblocks.m files on your system by typing

```
which('slblocks.m', '-all')
```

at the MATLAB command prompt. Copy any of the displayed files to your library's directory. Then, open the copy, edit it, following the instructions included in the file, and save the result. Finally, add your library's directory to the MATLAB path, if necessary. The next time you open the Library Browser, your library should appear among the libraries displayed in the browser.

# Modeling Equations

One of the most confusing issues for new Simulink users is how to model equations. Here are some examples that may improve your understanding of how to model equations.

## Converting Celsius to Fahrenheit

To model the equation that converts Celsius temperature to Fahrenheit

$$T_F = 9/5(T_C) + 32$$

First, consider the blocks needed to build the model:

- A Ramp block to input the temperature signal, from the Sources library
- A Constant block to define a constant of 32, also from the Sources library
- A Gain block to multiply the input signal by 9/5, from the Math library
- A Sum block to add the two quantities, also from the Math library
- A Scope block to display the output, from the Sinks library

Next, gather the blocks into your model window.

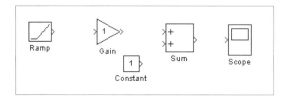

Assign parameter values to the Gain and Constant blocks by opening (double-clicking on) each block and entering the appropriate value. Then, click on the **Close** button to apply the value and close the dialog box.

Now, connect the blocks.

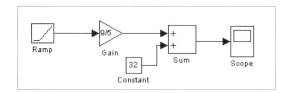

The Ramp block inputs Celsius temperature. Open that block and change the **Initial output** parameter to 0. The Gain block multiplies that temperature by the constant 9/5. The Sum block adds the value 32 to the result and outputs the Fahrenheit temperature.

Open the Scope block to view the output. Now, choose **Start** from the **Simulation** menu to run the simulation. The simulation will run for 10 seconds.

## Modeling a Simple Continuous System

To model the differential equation,

$$x'(t) = -2x(t) + u(t)$$

where $u(t)$ is a square wave with an amplitude of 1 and a frequency of 1 rad/sec. The Integrator block integrates its input, $x'$, to produce $x$. Other blocks needed in this model include a Gain block and a Sum block. To generate a square wave, use a Signal Generator block and select the Square Wave form but change the default units to radians/sec. Again, view the output using a Scope block. Gather the blocks and define the gain.

In this model, to reverse the direction of the Gain block, select the block, then use the **Flip Block** command from the **Format** menu. Also, to create the branch line from the output of the Integrator block to the Gain block, hold down the **Ctrl** key while drawing the line. For more information, see "Drawing a Branch Line" on page 4–24. Now you can connect all the blocks.

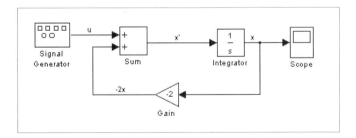

An important concept in this model is the loop that includes the Sum block, the Integrator block, and the Gain block. In this equation, $x$ is the output of the Integrator block. It is also the input to the blocks that compute $x'$, on which it is based. This relationship is implemented using a loop.

The Scope displays $x$ at each time step. For a simulation lasting 10 seconds, the output looks like this.

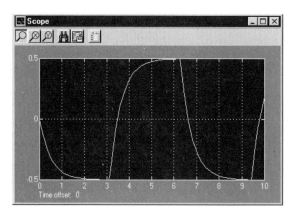

The equation you modeled in this example can also be expressed as a transfer function. The model uses the Transfer Fcn block, which accepts $u$ as input and outputs $x$. So, the block implements $x/u$. If you substitute $sx$ for $x'$ in the above equation, you get

$$sx = -2x + u$$

Solving for $x$ gives

$$x = u/(s+2)$$

or,

$$x/u = 1/(s+2)$$

The Transfer Fcn block uses parameters to specify the numerator and denominator coefficients. In this case, the numerator is 1 and the denominator is s+2. Specify both terms as vectors of coefficients of successively decreasing powers of s. In this case the numerator is [1] (or just 1) and the denominator is [1 2]. The model now becomes quite simple.

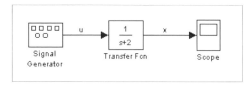

The results of this simulation are identical to those of the previous model.

# Saving a Model

You can save a model by choosing either the **Save** or **Save As** command from the **File** menu. Simulink saves the model by generating a specially formatted file called the *model file* (with the .mdl extension) that contains the block diagram and block properties.

If you are saving a model for the first time, use the **Save** command to provide a name and location to the model file. Model file names must start with a letter and can contain no more than 31 letters, numbers, and underscores.

If you are saving a model whose model file was previously saved, use the **Save** command to replace the file's contents or the **Save As** command to save the model with a new name or location.

Simulink follows this procedure while saving a model:

**1** If the mdl file for the model already exists, it is renamed as a temporary file.

**2** Simulink executes all block PreSaveFcn callback routines, then executes the block diagram's PreSaveFcn callback routine.

**3** Simulink writes the model file to a new file using the same name and an extension of mdl.

**4** Simulink executes all block PostSaveFcn callback routines, then executes the block diagram's PostSaveFcn callback routine.

**5** Simulink deletes the temporary file.

If an error occurs during this process, Simulink renames the temporary file to the name of the original model file, writes the current version of the model to a file with an .err extension, and issues an error message. Simulink performs steps 2 through 4 even if an error occurs in an earlier step.

# Printing a Block Diagram

You can print a block diagram by selecting **Print** from the **File** menu (on a Microsoft Windows system) or by using the `print` command in the MATLAB command window (on all platforms).

On a Microsoft Windows system, the **Print** menu item prints the block diagram in the current window.

## Print Dialog Box

When you select the **Print** menu item, the **Print** dialog box appears. The **Print** dialog box enables you to selectively print systems within your model. Using the dialog box, you can print:

- The current system only
- The current system and all systems above it in the model hierarchy
- The current system and all systems below it in the model hierarchy, with the option of looking into the contents of masked and library blocks
- All systems in the model, with the option of looking into the contents of masked and library blocks
- An overlay frame on each diagram

The portion of the **Print** dialog box that supports selective printing is similar on supported platforms. This figure shows how it looks on a Microsoft Windows system. In this figure, only the current system is to be printed.

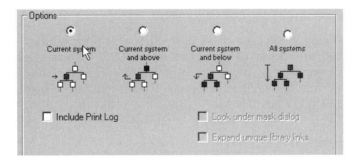

When you select either the **Current system and below** or **All systems** option, two check boxes become enabled. In this figure, **All systems** is selected.

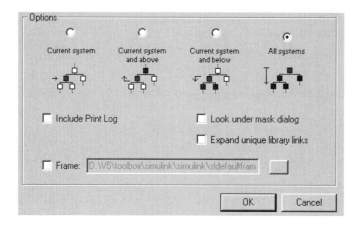

Selecting the **Look Under Mask Dialog** check box prints the contents of masked subsystems when encountered at or below the level of the current block. When printing all systems, the top-level system is considered the current block so Simulink looks under any masked blocks encountered.

Selecting the **Expand Unique Library Links** check box prints the contents of library blocks when those blocks are systems. Only one copy is printed regardless of how many copies of the block are contained in the model. For more information about libraries, see "Libraries" on page 4-57.

The print log lists the blocks and systems printed. To print the print log, select the **Include Print Log** check box.

Selecting the **Frame** check box prints a title block frame on each diagram. Enter the path to the title block frame in the adjacent edit box. You can create a customized title block frame, using MATLAB's frame editor. See `frameedit` in the online MATLAB reference for information on using the frame editor to create title block frames.

## Print Command

The format of the `print` command is

```
print -ssys -device filename
```

sys is the name of the system to be printed. The system name must be preceded by the s switch identifier and is the only required argument. sys must be open or must have been open during the current session. If the system name contains spaces or takes more than one line, you need to specify the name as a string. See the examples below.

*device* specifies a device type. For a list and description of device types, see *Using MATLAB Graphics*.

filename is the PostScript file to which the output is saved. If filename exists, it is replaced. If filename does not include an extension, an appropriate one is appended.

For example, this command prints a system named untitled.

```
print -suntitled
```

This command prints the contents of a subsystem named Sub1 in the current system.

```
print -sSub1
```

This command prints the contents of a subsystem named Requisite Friction.

```
print (['-sRequisite Friction'])
```

The next example prints a system named Friction Model, a subsystem whose name appears on two lines. The first command assigns the newline character to a variable; the second prints the system.

```
cr = sprintf('\n');
print (['-sFriction' cr 'Model'])
```

To print the currently selected subsystem, enter

```
print(['-s', gcb])
```

## Specifying Paper Size and Orientation

Simulink lets you specify the type and orientation of the paper used to print a model diagram. You can do this on all platforms by setting the model's PaperType and PaperOrientation properties, respectively, using the set_param command. You can set the paper orientation alone, using MATLAB's orient command. On Windows, the **Print** and **Printer Setup** dialog boxes lets you set the page type and orientation properties as well.

## Positioning and Sizing a Diagram

You can use a model's PaperPositionMode and PaperPosition parameters to position and size the model's diagram on the printed page. The value of the PaperPosition parameter is a vector of form [left bottom width height]. The first two elements specify the bottom left corner of a rectangular area on the page, measured from the page's bottom left corner. The last two elements specify the width and height of the rectangle. When the model's PaperPositionMode is manual, Simulink positions (and scales, if necessary) the model's diagram to fit inside the specified print rectangle. For example, the following commands

```
vdp
set_param('vdp', 'PaperType', 'usletter')
set_param('vdp', 'PaperOrientation', 'landscape')
set_param('vdp', 'PaperPositionMode', 'manual')
set_param('vdp', 'PaperPosition', [0.5 0.5 4 4])
print -svdp
```

print the block diagram of the vdp sample model in the lower left corner of a U.S. letter-size page in landscape orientation.

If PaperPositionMode is auto, Simulink centers the model diagram on the printed page, scaling the diagram, if necessary, to fit the page.

# Searching and Browsing Models

Simulink provides you with tools for searching and browsing models. These can be useful when you need to view or modify an object but do not know where it is located.

## Searching for Objects

To find a block, signal, state, or other object in a model, select **Find** from Simulink's **Edit** menu. Simulink displays the **Find** dialog box.

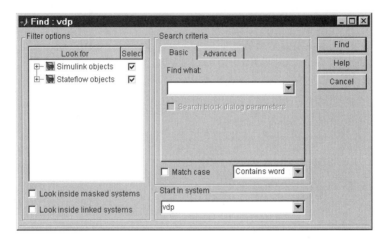

To find an object with the **Find** dialog box, first use the **Filter options** (see "Filter Options" on page 4-77) and **Search criteria** (see "Search Criteria" on page 4-77) panels to specify the characteristics of the object you want to find. Next, if you have more than one system or subsystem open, select the system or subsystem where you want the search to begin from the **Start in system** list. Finally, select the **Find** button. Simulink searches the selected system for objects that meet the criteria you have specified. Any objects that satisfy the criteria appear in the results panel at the bottom of the **Find** dialog box.

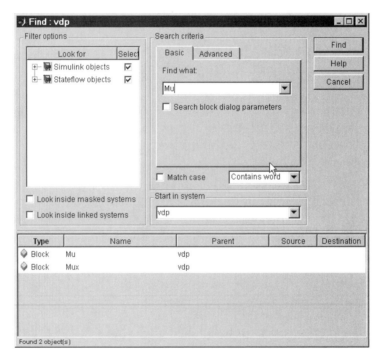

You can display an object by double-clicking its entry in the search results list. Simulink opens the system or subsystem that contains the object (if necessary) and highlights and selects the object. To sort the results list, click any of the buttons at the top of each column. For example, to sort the results by object type, click the **Type** button. Clicking a button once sorts the list in ascending order, clicking it twice sorts it in descending order. To display an object's parameters or properties, select the object in the list. Then press the right mouse button and select **Parameter** or **Properties** from the resulting context menu.

## Filter Options

The **Filter options** panel allows you to specify what kinds of objects to look for and where to search for them.

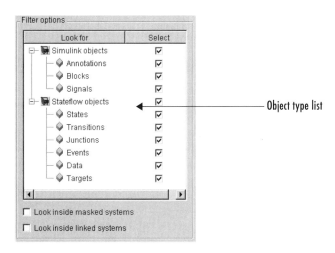

**Object type list.**  The object type list lists the types of objects that the Simulink can find. By unchecking a type, you can exclude it from the Finder's search.

**Look inside masked subsystem.**  Checking this option causes Simulink to look for objects inside of masked subsystems.

**Look inside linked systems.**  Checking this option causes Simulink to look for objects inside subsystems linked to libraries.

## Search Criteria

The **Search criteria** panel allows you to specify the criteria that objects must meet to satisfy your search request.

**Basic.**  The **Basic** panel allows you to search for objects whose name and, optionally, dialog parameters match a specified text string. Enter the search text in the panel's **Find what** field. To display previous search text, select the dropdown list button next to the **Find what** field. To reenter text, click it in the dropdown list. Check **Search block dialog parameters** if you want dialog parameters to be included in the search.

**Advanced.** The **Advanced** panel allows you to specify a set of as many as seven properties that an object must have to satisfy your search request.

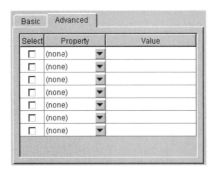

To specify a property, type its name in one of the cells in the **Property** column of the **Advanced** pane or select the property from the cell's property list. To display the list, select the down arrow button next to the cell. Next enter the value of the property in the **Value** column next to the property name. When you enter a property name, the **Finder** checks the check box next to the property name in the **Select** column. This indicates that the property is to be included in the search. If you want to exclude the property, uncheck the check box.

**Match case.** Check this option if you want Simulink to consider case when matching search text against the value of an object property.

**Other match options.** Next to the **Match case** option is a list that specifies other match options that you can select:

- `Match whole word`

  Specifies a match if the property value and the search text are identical except possibly for case.

- `Contains word`

  Specifies a match if a property value includes the search text.

• Regular expression

Specifies that the search text should be treated as a regular expression when matched against property values. The following characters have special meanings when they appear in a regular expression.

| Character | Meaning |
|---|---|
| ^ | Matches start of string. |
| $ | Matches end of string. |
| . | Matches any character. |
| \ | Escape character. Causes the next character to have its ordinary meaning. For example, the regular expression \.. matches .a and .2 and any other wo-character string that begins with a period. |
| * | Matches zero or more instances of the preceding character. For example, ba* matches b, ba, baa, etc. |
| + | Matches one or more instances of the preceding character. For example, ba+ matches ba, baa, etc. |
| [] | Indicates a set of characters that can match the current character. A hyphen can be used to indicate a range of characters. For example, [a-zA-Z0-9_]+ matches foo_bar1 but not foo$bar. A ^ indicates a match when the current character is not one of the following characters. For example, [^0-9] matches any character that is not a digit. |
| \w | Matches a word character (same as [a-z_A-Z0-9]). |
| \W | Matches a nonword character (same as [^a-z_A-Z0-9]). |
| \d | Matches a digit (same as [0-9]). |
| \D | Matches a nondigit (same as [^0-9]). |
| \s | Matches white space (same as [ \t\r\n\f]). |

| Character | Meaning |
|---|---|
| \S | Matches nonwhite space (same as [^ \t\r\n\f]). |
| \<WORD\> | Matches WORD where WORD is any string of word characters surrounded by white space. |

# The Model Browser

The Model Browser enables you to:

- Navigate a model hierarchically
- Open systems in a model directly
- Determine the blocks contained in a model
- Use your source control system to manage the model. Refer to "Interfacing with Source Control Systems" in the online MATLAB documentation.

The browser operates differently on Microsoft Windows and Linux platforms.

### Using the Model Browser on Windows

To display the Model Browser, select **Model Browser** from the Simulink **View** menu.

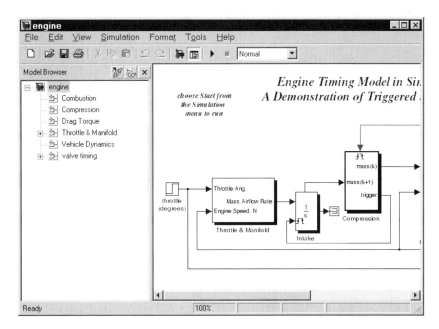

The model window splits into two panes. The left pane displays the browser, a tree-structured view of the block diagram displayed in the right pane.

**Note** The **Browser initially visible** preference causes Simulink to open models by default in the Model Browser. To set this preference, select **Preferences** from the Simulink **File** menu.

The top entry in the tree view corresponds to your model. A button next to the model name allows you to expand or contract the tree view. The expanded view shows the model's subsystems. A button next to a subsystem indicates that the subsystem itself contains subsystems. You can use the button to list the subsystem's children. To view the block diagram of the model or any subsystem displayed in the tree view, select the subsystem. You can use either the mouse or the keyboard to navigate quickly to any subsystem in the tree view.

**Navigating with the Mouse.** Click any subsystem visible in the tree view to select it. Click the + button next to any subsystem to list the subsystems that it contains. Click the button again to contract the entry.

**Navigating with the Keyboard.** Use the up/down arrows to move the current selection up or down the tree view. Use the left/right arrow or +/- keys on your numeric keypad to expand an entry that contains subsystems.

**Showing Library Links.** The Model Browser can include or omit library links from the tree view of a model. Use the Simulink **Preferences** dialog box to specify whether to display library links by default. To toggle display of library links, select **Show library links** from the **Model browser options** submenu of the Simulink **View** menu.

**Showing Masked Subsystems.** The Model Browser can include or omit masked subsystems from the tree view. If the tree view includes masked subsystems, selecting a masked subsystem in the tree view displays its block diagram in the diagram view. Use the Simulink **Preferences** dialog box to specify whether to display masked subsystems by default. To toggle display of masked subsystems, select **Look under masks** from the **Model browser options** submenu of the Simulink **View** menu.

## Using the Model Browser on Linux

To open the Model Browser, select **Show Browser** from the **File** menu. The Model Browser window appears, displaying information about the current model. This figure shows the Model Browser window displaying the contents of the clutch system.

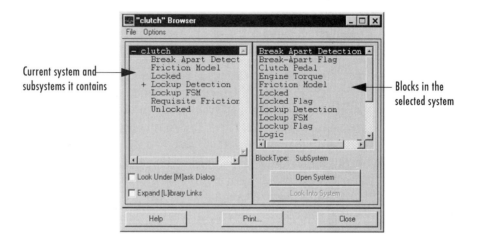

## Contents of the Browser Window

The Model Browser window consists of:

- The systems list. The list on the left contains the current system and the subsystems it contains, with the current system selected.
- The blocks list. The list on the right contains the names of blocks in the selected system. Initially, this window displays blocks in the top-level system.
- The **File** menu, which contains the **Print**, **Close Model**, and **Close Browser** menu items.
- The **Options** menu, which contains the menu items **Open System**, **Look Into System**, **Display Alphabetical/Hierarchical List**, **Expand All**, **Look Under Mask Dialog**, and **Expand Library Links**.
- The **Options** check boxes and buttons **Look Under [M]ask Dialog** and **Expand [L]ibrary Links** check boxes, and **Open System** and **Look Into System** buttons. By default, Simulink does not display contents of masked

blocks and blocks that are library links. These check boxes enable you to override the default.

- The block type of the selected block.

- Dialog box buttons **Help**, **Print**, and **Close**.

### Interpreting List Contents

Simulink identifies masked blocks, reference blocks, blocks with defined OpenFcn parameters, and systems that contain subsystems using these symbols before a block or system name:

- A plus sign (+) before a system name in the systems list indicates that the system is expandable, which means that it has systems beneath it. Double-click on the system name to expand the list and display its contents in the blocks list. When a system is expanded, a minus sign (–) appears before its name.

- [M] indicates that the block is masked, having either a mask dialog box or a mask workspace. For more information about masking, see Chapter 7, "Using Masks to Customize Blocks."

- [L] indicates that the block is a reference block. For more information, see "Connecting Blocks" on page 4-23.

- [O] indicates that an open function (OpenFcn) callback is defined for the block. For more information about block callbacks, see "Using Callback Routines" on page 4-50.

- [S] indicates that the system is a Stateflow block.

### Opening a System

You can open any block or system whose name appears in the blocks list. To open a system:

1 In the systems list, select by single-clicking on the name of the parent system that contains the system you want to open. The parent system's contents appear in the blocks list.

2 Depending on whether the system is masked, linked to a library block, or has an open function callback, you open it as follows:

- If the system has no symbol to its left, double-click on its name or select its name and click on the **Open System** button.

- If the system has an [M] or [O] before its name, select the system name and click on the **Look Into System** button.

## Looking into a Masked System or a Linked Block

By default, the Model Browser considers masked systems (identified by [M]) and linked blocks (identified by [L]) as blocks and not subsystems. If you click on **Open System** while a masked system or linked block is selected, the Model Browser displays the system or block's dialog box (**Open System** works the same way as double-clicking on the block in a block diagram). Similarly, if the block's OpenFcn callback parameter is defined, clicking on **Open System** while that block is selected executes the callback function.

You can direct the Model Browser to look beyond the dialog box or callback function by selecting the block in the blocks list, then clicking on **Look Into System**. The Model Browser displays the underlying system or block.

## Displaying List Contents Alphabetically

By default, the systems list indicates the hierarchy of the model. Systems that contain systems are preceded with a plus sign (+). When those systems are expanded, the Model Browser displays a minus sign (−) before their names. To display systems alphabetically, select the **Display Alphabetical List** menu item on the **Options** menu.

# Ending a Simulink Session

Terminate a Simulink session by closing all Simulink windows.

Terminate a MATLAB session by choosing one of these commands from the **File** menu:

- On a Microsoft Windows system: **Exit MATLAB**
- On a Linux system: **Quit MATLAB**

**5**

# Running a Simulation

# Introduction

You can run a simulation either by using Simulink menu commands or by entering commands in the MATLAB command window.

Many users use menu commands while they develop and refine their models, then enter commands in the MATLAB command window to run the simulation in "batch" mode.

## Using Menu Commands

Running a simulation using menu commands is easy and interactive. These commands let you select an ordinary differential equation (ODE) solver and define simulation parameters without having to remember command syntax. An important advantage is that you can perform certain operations interactively while a simulation is running. You can:

- Modify many simulation parameters, including the stop time, the solver, and the maximum step size.
- Change the solver.
- Simulate another system at the same time.
- Click on a line to see the signal carried on that line on a floating (unconnected) Scope or Display block.
- Modify the parameters of a block, as long as you do not cause a change in:
  - The number of states, inputs, or outputs
  - The sample time
  - The number of zero crossings
  - The vector length of any block parameters
  - The length of the internal block work vectors

You cannot make changes to the structure of the model, such as adding or deleting lines or blocks, during a simulation. If you need to make these kinds of changes, you need to stop the simulation, make the change, then start the simulation again to see the results of the change.

# Running a Simulation Using Menu Commands

This section discusses how to use Simulink menu commands and the **Simulation Parameters** dialog box to run a simulation.

## Setting Simulation Parameters and Choosing the Solver

You set the simulation parameters and select the solver by choosing **Parameters** from the **Simulation** menu. Simulink displays the **Simulation Parameters** dialog box, which uses three "panes" to manage simulation parameters:

- The **Solver** pane allows you to set the start and stop times, choose the solver and specify solver parameters, and choose some output options.
- The **Workspace I/O** pane manages input from and output to the MATLAB workspace.
- The **Diagnostics** pane allows you to select the level of warning messages displayed during a simulation.

Each pane of the dialog box, including the parameters you set on the pane, is discussed in detail in "The Simulation Parameters Dialog Box" on page 5–7.

You can specify parameters as valid MATLAB expressions, consisting of constants, workspace variable names, MATLAB functions, and mathematical operators.

## Applying the Simulation Parameters

After you have set the simulation parameters and selected the solver, you are ready to apply them to your model. Press the **Apply** button on the bottom of the dialog box to apply the parameters to the model. To apply the parameters and close the dialog box, press the **Close** button.

## Starting the Simulation

After you have applied the solver and simulation parameters to your model, you are ready to run the simulation. Select **Start** from the **Simulation** menu to run the simulation. You can also use the keyboard shortcut, **Ctrl+T**. When you select **Start**, the menu item changes to **Stop**.

Your computer beeps to signal the completion of the simulation.

---

**Note** A common mistake that new Simulink users make is to start a simulation while the Simulink block library is the active window. Make sure your model window is the active window before starting a simulation.

---

To stop a simulation, choose **Stop** from the **Simulation** menu. The keyboard shortcut for stopping a simulation is **Ctrl+T**, the same as for starting a simulation.

You can suspend a running simulation by choosing **Pause** from the **Simulation** menu. When you select **Pause**, the menu item changes to **Continue**. You proceed with a suspended simulation by choosing **Continue**.

If the model includes any blocks that write output to a file or to the workspace, or if you select output options on the **Simulation Parameters** dialog box, Simulink writes the data when the simulation is terminated or suspended.

## Simulation Diagnostics Dialog Box

If errors occur during a simulation, Simulink halts the simulation and displays the errors in the **Simulation Diagnostics** dialog box.

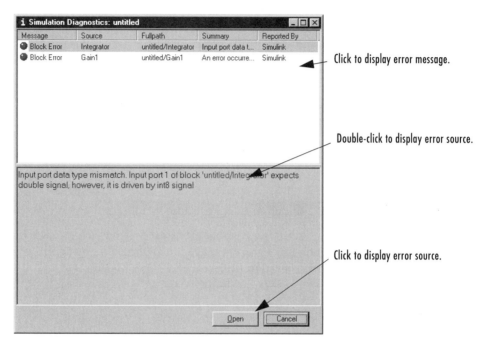

Click to display error message.

Double-click to display error source.

Click to display error source.

The dialog box has two panes. The upper pane consist of columns that display the following information for each error.

**Message.**  Message type (for example, block error, warning, log)

**Source.**  Name of the model element (for example, a block) that caused the error.

**Fullpath.**  Path of the element that caused the error.

**Summary.**  Error message abbreviated to fit in the column.

**Reported by.**  Component that reported the error (for example, Simulink, Stateflow, Real-Time Workshop, etc.).

The lower pane initially contains the full content of the first error message listed in the top pane. You can display the content of other messages by single-clicking on their entries in the upper pane.

In addition to displaying the **Simulation Diagnostics** dialog box, Simulink also opens (if necessary) the diagram that contains the error source and highlights the source.

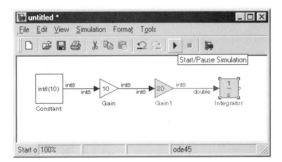

You can similarly display other error sources by double-clicking on the corresponding error message in the top pane, by double-clicking on the name of the error source in the error message (highlighted in blue), or by selecting the **Open** button on the dialog box.

# The Simulation Parameters Dialog Box

This section discusses the simulation parameters, which you specify either on the **Simulation Parameters** dialog box or using the sim and simset commands (see "Running a Simulation from the Command Line" in the online Simulink help). Parameters are described as they appear on the dialog box panes.

This table summarizes the actions performed by the dialog box buttons that appear on the bottom of each dialog box pane.

**Table 5-1: Simulation Parameters Dialog Box Buttons**

| Button | Action |
|--------|--------|
| **OK** | Applies the parameter values and closes the dialog box. During a simulation, the parameter values are applied immediately. |
| **Cancel** | Changes the parameter values back to the values they had when the dialog box was most recently opened and closes the dialog box. |
| **Help** | Displays help text for the dialog box pane. |
| **Apply** | Applies the current parameter values and keeps the dialog box open. During a simulation, the parameter values are applied immediately. |

## The Solver Pane

The **Solver** pane appears when you first choose **Parameters** from the **Simulation** menu or when you select the **Solver** tab.

The **Solver** pane allows you to:

- Set the simulation start and stop times
- Choose the solver and specify its parameters
- Select output options

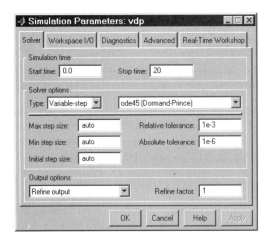

## Simulation Time

You can change the start time and stop time for the simulation by entering new values in the **Start time** and **Stop time** fields. The default start time is 0.0 seconds and the default stop time is 10.0 seconds.

Simulation time and actual clock time are not the same. For example, running a simulation for 10 seconds will usually not take 10 seconds. The amount of time it takes to run a simulation depends on many factors, including the model's complexity, the solver's step sizes, and the computer's clock speed.

## Solvers

Simulation of Simulink models involves the numerical integration of sets of ordinary differential equations (ODEs). Simulink provides a number of solvers for the simulation of such equations. Because of the diversity of dynamic system behavior, some solvers may be more efficient than others at solving a particular problem. To obtain accurate and fast results, take care when choosing the solver and setting parameters.

You can choose between variable-step and fixed-step solvers. *Variable-step solvers* can modify their step sizes during the simulation. They provide error control and zero crossing detection. *Fixed-step solvers* take the same step size during the simulation. They provide no error control and do not locate zero crossings. For a thorough discussion of solvers, see the MATLAB documentation.

**Default solvers.** If you do not choose a solver, Simulink chooses one based on whether your model has states:

- If the model has continuous states, `ode45` is used. `ode45` is an excellent general purpose solver. However, if you know that your system is stiff and if `ode45` is not providing acceptable results, try `ode15s`. For a definition of stiff, see the note at the end of the section "Variable-step solvers" on page 5-9.

- If the model has no continuous states, Simulink uses the variable-step solver called `discrete` and displays a message indicating that it is not using `ode45`. Simulink also provides a fixed-step solver called `discrete`. This model shows the difference between the two `discrete` solvers.

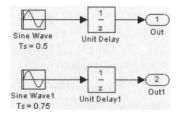

With sample times of 0.5 and 0.75, the *fundamental sample time* for the model is 0.25 second. The difference between the variable-step and the fixed-step `discrete` solvers is the time vector that each generates.

The fixed-step `discrete` solver generates this time vector.

```
[0.0 0.25 0.5 0.75 1.0 1.25 ...]
```

The variable-step `discrete` solver generates this time vector.

```
[0.0 0.5 0.75 1.0 1.5 2.0 2.25 ...]
```

The step size of the fixed-step `discrete` solver is the fundamental sample time. The variable-step `discrete` solver takes the largest possible steps.

**Variable-step solvers.** You can choose these variable-step solvers: `ode45`, `ode23`, `ode113`, `ode15s`, `ode23s`, and `discrete`. The default is `ode45` for systems with states, or `discrete` for systems with no states:

- `ode45` is based on an explicit Runge-Kutta (4,5) formula, the Dormand-Prince pair. It is a *one-step* solver; that is, in computing $y(t_n)$, it needs only the solution at the immediately preceding time point, $y(t_{n-1})$. In general, `ode45` is the best solver to apply as a "first try" for most problems.

- ode23 is also based on an explicit Runge-Kutta (2,3) pair of Bogacki and Shampine. It may be more efficient than ode45 at crude tolerances and in the presence of mild stiffness. ode23 is a one-step solver.

- ode113 is a variable order Adams-Bashforth-Moulton PECE solver. It may be more efficient than ode45 at stringent tolerances. ode113 is a *multistep* solver; that is, it normally needs the solutions at several preceding time points to compute the current solution.

- ode15s is a variable order solver based on the numerical differentiation formulas (NDFs). These are related to but are more efficient than the backward differentiation formulas, BDFs (also known as Gear's method). Like ode113, ode15s is a multistep method solver. If you suspect that a problem is stiff or if ode45 failed or was very inefficient, try ode15s.

- ode23s is based on a modified Rosenbrock formula of order 2. Because it is a one-step solver, it may be more efficient than ode15s at crude tolerances. It can solve some kinds of stiff problems for which ode15s is not effective.

- ode23t is an implementation of the trapezoidal rule using a "free" interpolant. Use this solver if the problem is only moderately stiff and you need a solution without numerical damping.

- ode23tb is an implementation of TR-BDF2, an implicit Runge-Kutta formula with a first stage that is a trapezoidal rule step and a second stage that is a backward differentiation formula of order two. By construction, the same iteration matrix is used in evaluating both stages. Like ode23s, this solver may be more efficient than ode15s at crude tolerances.

- discrete (variable-step) is the solver Simulink chooses when it detects that your model has no continuous states.

---

**Note** For a *stiff* problem, solutions can change on a time scale that is very short compared to the interval of integration, but the solution of interest changes on a much longer time scale. Methods not designed for stiff problems are ineffective on intervals where the solution changes slowly because they use time steps small enough to resolve the fastest possible change. Jacobian matrices are generated numerically for ode15s and ode23s. For more information, see Shampine, L. F., *Numerical Solution of Ordinary Differential Equations*, Chapman & Hall, 1994.

---

**Fixed-step solvers.** You can choose these fixed-step solvers: ode5, ode4, ode3, ode2, ode1, and discrete:

- ode5 is the fixed-step version of ode45, the Dormand-Prince formula.
- ode4 is RK4, the fourth-order Runge-Kutta formula.
- ode3 is the fixed-step version of ode23, the Bogacki-Shampine formula.
- ode2 is Heun's method, also known as the improved Euler formula.
- ode1 is Euler's method.
- discrete (fixed-step) is a fixed-step solver that performs no integration. It is suitable for models having no states and for which zero crossing detection and error control are not important.

If you think your simulation may be providing unsatisfactory results, see "Improving Simulation Performance and Accuracy" on page 5–33.

## Solver Options

The default solver parameters provide accurate and efficient results for most problems. In some cases, however, tuning the parameters can improve performance. (For more information about tuning these parameters, see "Improving Simulation Performance and Accuracy" on page 5–33). You can tune the selected solver by changing parameter values on the **Solver** pane.

## Step Sizes

For variable-step solvers, you can set the maximum and suggested initial step size parameters. By default, these parameters are automatically determined, indicated by the value auto.

For fixed-step solvers, you can set the fixed step size. The default is also auto.

**Maximum step size.** The **Max step size** parameter controls the largest time step the solver can take. The default is determined from the start and stop times.

$$h_{max} = \frac{t_{stop} - t_{start}}{50}$$

Generally, the default maximum step size is sufficient. If you are concerned about the solver missing significant behavior, change the parameter to prevent the solver from taking too large a step. If the time span of the simulation is very long, the default step size may be too large for the solver to find the solution.

Also, if your model contains periodic or nearly periodic behavior and you know the period, set the maximum step size to some fraction (such as 1/4) of that period.

In general, for more output points, change the refine factor, not the maximum step size. For more information, see "Refine output" on page 5–15.

**Initial step size.** By default, the solvers select an initial step size by examining the derivatives of the states at the start time. If the first step size is too large, the solver may step over important behavior. The initial step size parameter is a *suggested* first step size. The solver tries this step size but reduces it if error criteria are not satisfied.

**Minimum step size.** Specifies the smallest time step the solver can take. If the solver needs to take a smaller step to meet error tolerances, it issues a warning indicating the current effective relative tolerance. This parameter can be either a real number greater than zero or a two-element vector where the first element is the minimum step size and the second element is the maximum number of minimum step size warnings to be issued before issuing an error. Setting the second element to zero results in an error the first time the solver must take a step smaller than the specified minimum. This is equivalent to changing the minimum step size violation diagnostic to error on the **Diagnostics** panel. Setting the second element to -1 results in an unlimited number of warnings. This is also the default if the input is a scalar. The default values for this parameter are a minimum step size on the order of machine precision and an unlimited number of warnings.

### Error Tolerances

The solvers use standard local error control techniques to monitor the error at each time step. During each time step, the solvers compute the state values at the end of the step and also determine the *local error*, the estimated error of these state values. They then compare the local error to the *acceptable error*, which is a function of the relative tolerance ($rtol$) and absolute tolerance ($atol$). If the error is greater than the acceptable error for *any* state, the solver reduces the step size and tries again:

- *Relative tolerance* measures the error relative to the size of each state. The relative tolerance represents a percentage of the state's value. The default, 1e-3, means that the computed state will be accurate to within 0.1%.

- *Absolute tolerance* is a threshold error value. This tolerance represents the acceptable error as the value of the measured state approaches zero.

The error for the ith state, $e_i$, is required to satisfy

$$e_i \le max(rtol \times |x_i|, atol_i)$$

The following figure shows a plot of a state and the regions in which the acceptable error is determined by the relative tolerance and the absolute tolerance.

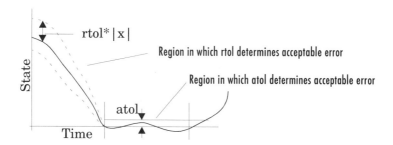

If you specify auto (the default), Simulink sets the absolute tolerance for each state initially to 1e-6. As the simulation progresses, Simulink resets the absolute tolerance for each state to the maximum value that the state has assumed thus far times the relative tolerance for that state. Thus, if a state goes from 0 to 1 and reltol is 1e-3, then by the end of the simulation the abstol is set to 1e-3 also. If a state goes from 0 to 1000, then the abstol is set to 1.

If the computed setting is not suitable, you can determine an appropriate setting yourself. You might have to run a simulation more than once to determine an appropriate value for the absolute tolerance. If the magnitudes of the states vary widely, it might be appropriate to specify different absolute tolerance values for different states. You can do this on the Integrator block's dialog box.

### The Maximum Order for ode15s

The ode15s solver is based on NDF formulas of order one through five. Although the higher order formulas are more accurate, they are less stable. If your model is stiff and requires more stability, reduce the maximum order to 2 (the highest order for which the NDF formula is A-stable). When you choose the ode15s solver, the dialog box displays this parameter.

As an alternative, you might try using the ode23s solver, which is a fixed-step, lower order (and A-stable) solver.

### Multitasking Options

If you select a fixed-step solver, the **Solver** pane of the **Simulation Parameters** dialog box displays a **Mode** options list. The list allows you to select one of the following simulation modes.

**MultiTasking.** This mode issues an error if it detects an illegal sample rate transition between blocks, that is, a direct connection between blocks operating at different sample rates. In real-time multitasking systems, illegal sample rate transitions between tasks can result in a task's output not being available when needed by another task. By checking for such transitions, multitasking mode helps you to create valid models of real-world multitasking systems, where sections of your model represent concurrent tasks.

Use *rate transition* blocks to eliminate illegal rate transitions from your model. Simulink provides two such blocks: Unit Delay and Zero-Order Hold. To eliminate an illegal slow-to-fast transition, insert a Unit Delay block running at the slow rate between the slow output port and the fast input port. To eliminate an illegal fast-to-slow transition, insert a Zero-Order Hold block running at the slow rate between the fast output port and the slow input port. For more information, see Chapter 7, "Models with Multiple Sample Rates," in the *Real-Time Workshop Users Guide*.

**SingleTasking.** This mode does not check for sample rate transitions among blocks. This mode is useful when you are modeling a single-tasking system. In such systems, task synchronization is not an issue.

**Auto.** This option causes Simulink to use single-tasking mode if all blocks operate at the same rate and multitasking mode if the model contains blocks operating at different rates.

### Output Options

The **Output options** area of the dialog box enables you to control how much output the simulation generates. You can choose from three options:

- Refine output

- Produce additional output
- Produce specified output only

**Refine output.** The **Refine output** choice provides additional output points when the simulation output is too coarse. This parameter provides an integer number of output points between time steps; for example, a refine factor of 2 provides output midway between the time steps, as well as at the steps. The default refine factor is 1.

To get smoother output, it is much faster to change the refine factor instead of reducing the step size. When the refine factor is changed, the solvers generate additional points by evaluating a continuous extension formula at those points. Changing the refine factor does not change the steps used by the solver.

The refine factor applies to variable-step solvers and is most useful when using ode45. The ode45 solver is capable of taking large steps; when graphing simulation output, you may find that output from this solver is not sufficiently smooth. If this is the case, run the simulation again with a larger refine factor. A value of 4 should provide much smoother results.

---

**Note** This option will not help the solver to locate zero crossings (see "Zero Crossing Detection" on page 3-13).

---

**Produce additional output.** The **Produce additional output** choice enables you to specify directly those additional times at which the solver generates output. When you select this option, Simulink displays an **Ouput Times** field on the **Solver** pane. Enter a MATLAB expression in this field that evaluates to an additional time or a vector of additional times. The additional output is produced using a continuous extension formula at the additional times. Unlike the refine factor, this option changes the simulation step size so that time steps coincide with the times that you have specified for additional output.

**Produce specified output only.** The **Produce specified output only** choice provides simulation output *only* at the specified output times. This option changes the simulation step size so that time steps coincide with the times that you have specified for producing output. This choice is useful when comparing different simulations to ensure that the simulations produce output at the same times.

**Comparing Output options.** A sample simulation generates output at these times.

```
0, 2.5, 5, 8.5, 10
```

Choosing **Refine output** and specifying a refine factor of 2 generates output at these times.

```
0, 1.25, 2.5, 3.75, 5, 6.75, 8.5, 9.25, 10
```

Choosing the **Produce additional output** option and specifying [0:10] generates output at these times

```
0, 1, 2, 3, 4, 5, 6, 7, 8, 9, 10
```

and perhaps at additional times, depending on the step-size chosen by the variable-step solver.

Choosing the **Produce Specified Output Only** option and specifying [0:10] generates output at these times.

```
0, 1, 2, 3, 4, 5, 6, 7, 8, 9, 10
```

In general, you should specify output points as integers times a fundamental step size, e.g.,

```
[1:100]*0.01
```

is more accurate than

```
[1:0.01:100]
```

# The Workspace I/O Pane

You can direct simulation output to workspace variables and get input and initial states from the workspace. On the **Simulation Parameters** dialog box, select the **Workspace I/O** tab. This pane appears.

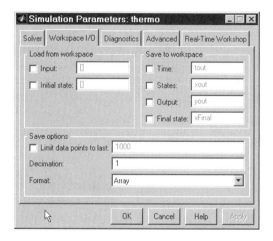

## Loading Input from the Base Workspace

Simulink can apply input from a model's base workspace to the model's top-level inports during a simulation run. To specify this option, check the **Input** box in the **Load from workspace** area of the **Workspace I/O** pane. Then, enter an external input specification (see below) in the adjacent edit box and select **Apply**.

The external (i.e., from workspace) input can take any of the following forms.

**Array.**  To use this format, check **Input** in the **Load from workspace** pane and select the Matrix option from the **Format** list on the **Workspace I/O** pane. Selecting this option causes Simulink to evaluate the expression next to the **Input** check box and use the result as the input to the model.

The expression must evaluate to a real (noncomplex) matrix of data type double. The first column of the matrix must be a vector of times in ascending order. The remaining columns specify input values. In particular, each column represents the input for a different Inport block signal (in sequential order) and each row is the input value for the corresponding time point. Simulink linearly interpolates or extrapolates input values as necessary, if the **Interpolate data** option is selected for the corresponding inport.

The total number of columns of the input matrix must equal n + 1, where n is the total number of signals entering the model's inports.

The default input expression for a model is [t,u] and the default input format is Matrix. So if you define t and u in the base workspace, you need only check the **Input** option to input data from the model's base workspace. For example, suppose that a model has two inports, one of which accepts two signals and the other of which accepts one signal. Also, suppose that the base workspace defines u and t as follows.

```
t = (0:0.1:1)';
u = [sin(t), cos(t), 4*cos(t)];
```

---

**Note** The matrix input format allows you to load only real (noncomplex) scalar or vector data of type double. Use the structure format to input complex data, matrix (2-D) data, and/or data types other than double.

---

**Structure with time.** Simulink can read data from the workspace in the form of a structure whose name is specified in the **Input** text field. The input structure must have two top-level fields: time and signals. The time field contains a column vector of the simulation times. The signals field contains an array of substructures, each of which corresponds to a model input port.

Each signals substructure must contain two fields named values and dimensions, respectively. The values field must contain an array of inputs for the corresponding input port where each input corresponds to a time point specified by the time field. The dimensions field specifies the dimension(s) of the input. If each input is a scalar or vector (1-D array) value, the dimensions field must be a scalar value that specifies the length of the vector (1 for a scalar). If each input is a matrix (2-D array), the dimensions field must be a two-element vector whose first element specifies the number of rows in the matrix and whose second element specifies the number of columns.

If the inputs for a port are scalar or vector values, the values field must be an M-by-N array where M is the number of time points specified by the time field and N is the length of each vector value. For example, the following code creates an input structure for loading 11 time samples of a two-element signal vector of type int8 into a model with a single input port.

```
a.time = (0:0.1:1)';
c1 = int8([0:1:10]');
c2 = int8([0:10:100]');
a.signals(1).values = [c1 c2];
a.signals(1).dimensions = 2;
```

To load this data into the model's inport, you would check the **Input** option on the **Workspace I/O** pane and enter a in the input expression field.

If the inputs for a port are matrices (2-D arrays), the values field must be an Mx N-by-T array where M and N are the dimensions of each matrix input and T is the number of time points. For example, suppose that you want to input 51 time samples of a 4-by-5 matrix signal into one of your model's input ports. Then, the corresponding dimensions field of the workspace structure must equal [4 5] and the values array must have the dimensions 4-by-5-by-51.

As another example, consider the following model, which has two inputs.

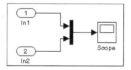

Suppose that you want to input a sine wave into the first port and a cosine wave into the second port. To do this, define a vector, a, as follows in the base workspace.

```
a.time = (0:0.1:1)';
a.signals(1).values = sin(a.time);
a.signals(1).dimensions = 1;
a.signals(2).values = cos(a.time);
a.signals(2).dimensions = 1;
```

Then, check the **Input** box for this model, enter a in the adjacent text field, and select StructureWithTime as the I/O format.

---

**Note** Simulink can read back simulation data saved to the workspace in the **Structure with time** output format. See "Structure with time" on page 5-22 for more information.

---

**Structure.** The structure format is the same as the **Structure with time** format except that `time` field is empty. For example, in the preceding example, you could set the time field as follows.

```
a.time = []
```

In this case, Simulink reads the input for the first time step from the first element of an inport's value array, the value for the second time step from the second element of the value array, etc.

---

**Note** Simulink can read back simulation data saved to the workspace in the **Structure** output format. See "Structure" on page 5-23 for more information.

---

**Per-Port Structures.** This format consists of a separate structure-with-time or structure-without-time for each port. Each port's input data structure has only one `signals` field. To specify this option, enter the names of the structures in the **Input** text field as a comma-separated list `in1`, `in2`, `...`, `inN`, where `in1` is the data for your model's first port, `in2` for the second inport, and so on.

**Time Expression.** The time expression can be any MATLAB expression that evaluates to a row vector equal in length to the number of signals entering the model's inports. For example, suppose that a model has one vector inport that accepts two signals. Furthermore, suppose that `timefcn` is a user-defined function that returns a row vector two elements long. The following are valid input time expressions for such a model.

```
'[3*sin(t), cos(2*t)]'
```

```
'4*timefcn(w*t)+7'
```

Simulink evaluates the expression at each step of the simulation, applying the resulting values to the model's inports. Note that Simulink defines the variable `t` when it runs the simulation. Also, you can omit the time variable in expressions for functions of one variable. For example, Simulink interprets the expression `sin` as `sin(t)`.

## Saving Output to the Workspace

You can specify return variables by selecting the **Time**, **States**, and/or **Output** check boxes in the **Save to workspace** area of this dialog box pane. Specifying return variables causes Simulink to write values for the time, state, and output trajectories (as many as are selected) into the workspace.

To assign values to different variables, specify those variable names in the field to the right of the check boxes. To write output to more than one variable, specify the variable names in a comma-separated list. Simulink saves the simulation times in the vector specified in the **Save to Workspace** area.

---

**Note** Simulink saves the output to the workspace at the base sample rate of the model. Use a To Workspace block if you want to save output at a different sample rate.

---

The **Save options** area enables you to specify the format and restrict the amount of output saved.

Format options for model states and outputs are listed below.

**Array.** If you select this option, Simulink saves a model's states and outputs in a state and output array, respectively.

The state matrix has the name specified in the **Save to Workspace** area (for example, `xout`). Each row of the state matrix corresponds to a time sample of the model's states. Each column corresponds to an element of a state. For example, suppose that your model has two continuous states, each of which is a two-element vector. Then the first two elements of each row of the state matrix contains a time sample of the first state vector. The last two elements of each row contain a time sample of the second state vector.

The model output matrix has the name specified in the **Save to Workspace** area (for example, `yout`). Each column corresponds to a model outport, each row to the outputs at a specific time.

**Note** You can use array format to save your model's outputs and states only if the outputs are either all scalars or all vectors (or all matrices for states), are either all real or all complex, and are all of the same data type. Use the Structure or StructureWithTime output formats (see the following) if your model's outputs and states do not meet these conditions.

**Structure with time.** If you select this format, Simulink saves the model's states and outputs in structures having the names specified in the **Save to Workspace** area (for example, xout and yout).

The structure used to save outputs has two top-level fields: time and signals. The time field contains a vector of the simulation times. The signals field contains an array of substructures, each of which corresponds to a model outport. Each substructure has four fields: values, dimensions, label, and blockName. The values field contains the outputs for the corresponding outport. If the outputs are scalars or vectors, the values field is a matrix each of whose rows represents an output at the time specified by the corresponding element of the time vector. If the outputs are matrix (2-D) values, the values field is a 3-D array of dimensions M-by-N-by-T where M-by-N is the dimensions of the output signal and T is the number of output samples. If T = 1, MATLAB drops the last dimension. Therefore, the value field will be an M-by-N matrix. The dimensions field specifies the dimensions of the output signal. The label field specifies the label of the signal connected to the outport or the type of state (continuous or discrete). The blockName field specifies the name of the corresponding outport or block with states.

The structure used to save states has a similar organization. The states structure has two top-level fields: time and signals. The time field contains a vector of the simulation times. The signals field contains an array of substructures, each of which corresponds to one of the model's states. Each signals structure has four fields: values, dimension, label, and blockName. The values field contains time samples of a state of the block specified by the blockName field. The label field for built-in blocks indicates the type of state: either CSTATE (continuous state) or DSTATE (discrete state). For S-Function blocks, the label contains whatever name is assigned to the state by the S-Function block.

The time samples of a state are stored in the `values` field as a matrix of values. Each row corresponds to a time sample. Each element of a row corresponds to an element of the state. If the state is a matrix, the matrix is stored in the `values` array in column-major order. For example, suppose that the model includes a 2-by-2 matrix state and that Simulink logs 51 samples of the state during a simulation run . Then the `values` field for this state would contain a 51-by-4 matrix where each row corresponds to a time sample of the state and where the first two elements of each row corresponds to the first column of the sample and the last two elements corresponds to the second column of the sample.

**Structure.** This format is the same as the preceding except that Simulink does not store simulation times in the `time` field of the saved structure.

**Per-Port Structures.** This format consists of a separate structure-with-time or structure-without-time for each output port. Each output data structure has only one `signals` field. To specify this option, enter the names of the structures in the **Output** text field as a comma-separated list `out1`, `out2`, `...`, `outN`, where `out1` is the data for your model's first port, `out2` for the second inport, and so on.

To set a limit on the number of data samples saved, select the check box labeled **Limit data points to last** and specify the number of samples to save. To apply a decimation factor, enter a value in the field to the right of the **Decimation** label. For example, a value of 2 saves every other point generated.

## Loading and Saving States

Initial conditions, which are applied to the system at the start of the simulation, are generally set in the blocks. You can override initial conditions set in the blocks by specifying them in the **States** area of this pane.

You can also save the final states for the current simulation run and apply them to a subsequent simulation run. This feature might be useful when you want to save a steady-state solution and restart the simulation at that known state. The states are saved in the format that you select in the Save options area of the Workspace I/O pane.

To save the final states (the values of the states at the termination of the simulation), select the **Final State** check box and enter a variable in the adjacent edit field.

To load states, select the **Initial State** check box and specify the name of a variable that contains the initial state values. This variable can be a matrix or a structure of the same form as is used to save final states. This allows Simulink to set the initial states for the current session to the final states saved in previous session, using the **Structure** or **Structure with time** format.

If the check box is not selected or the state array is empty ( [ ] ), Simulink uses the initial conditions defined in the blocks.

## The Diagnostics Pane

You can indicate the desired action for many types of events or conditions that can be encountered during a simulation by selecting the **Diagnostics** tab on the **Simulation Parameters** dialog box. This dialog box appears.

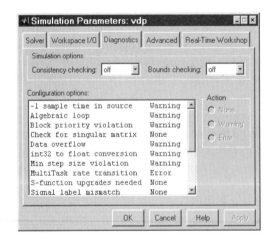

The dialog box includes the following options.

### Consistency Checking

Consistency checking is a debugging tool that validates certain assumptions made by Simulink's ODE solvers. Its main use is to make sure that S-functions adhere to the same rules as Simulink built-in blocks. Because consistency checking results in a significant decrease in performance (up to 40%), it should generally be set to off. Use consistency checking to validate your S-functions and to help you determine the cause of unexpected simulation results.

To perform efficient integration, Simulink saves (caches) certain values from one time step for use in the next time step. For example, the derivatives at the end of a time step can generally be reused at the start of the next time step. The solvers take advantage of this to avoid redundant derivative calculations.

Another purpose of consistency checking is to ensure that blocks produce constant output when called with a given value of $t$ (time). This is important for the stiff solvers (ode23s and ode15s) because, while calculating the Jacobian, the block's output functions may be called many times at the same value of $t$.

When consistency checking is enabled, Simulink recomputes the appropriate values and compares them to the cached values. If the values are not the same, a consistency error occurs. Simulink compares computed values for these quantities:

- Outputs
- Zero crossings
- Derivatives
- States

### Bounds Checking

This option causes Simulink to check whether a block writes outside the memory allocated to it during simulation. Typically this can happen only if your model includes a user-written S-function that has a bug. If enabled, this check is performed for every block in the model every time the block is executed. As a result, enabling this option slows down model execution considerably. Thus, to avoid slowing down model execution needlessly, you should enable the option only if you suspect that your model contains a user-written S-function that has a bug. See *Writing S-Functions* for more information on using this option.

### Configuration options

This control lists abnormal types of events that can occur during execution of the model For each event type, you can choose whether you want no message, a warning message, or an error message. A warning message does not terminate a simulation, but an error message does.

| Event | Description |
|-------|-------------|
| `-1 sample time in source` | A source block (e.g., a Sine Wave block) specifies a sample time of -1. |
| `Algebraic loop` | Simulink detected an algebraic loop while simulating the model. See "Algebraic Loops" on page 3–17 for more information. |
| `Block Priority Violation` | Simulink detected a block priority specification error while simulating the model. |
| `Check for singular matrix` | The Product block detected a singular matrix while inverting one of its inputs in matrix multiplication mode. |
| `Data overflow` | The value of a signal or parameter is too large to be represented by the signal or parameter's data type. |
| `int32 to float conversion` | A 32-bit integer value was converted to a floating-point value. Such a conversion can result in a loss of precision. |
| `Min step size violation` | The next simulation step is smaller than minimum step size specified for the model. This can occur if the specified error tolerance for the model requires a step size smaller than the specified minimum step size. See "Step Sizes" on page 5–11 and "Error Tolerances" on page 5–12 for more information. |
| `Multitask rate transition` | An invalid rate transition occurred between two blocks operating in multitasking mode (see "Multitasking Options" on page 5-14). |
| `S-function upgrades needed` | A block was encountered that has not been upgraded to use features of the current release. |

| Event | Description  (Continued) |
|---|---|
| Signal label mismatch | The simulation encountered virtual signals that have a common source signal but different labels (see "Virtual Signals" on page 4–30). |
| SingleTask rate transition | A rate transition occurred between two blocks operating in single-tasking mode (see "Multitasking Options" on page 5-14). |
| Unconnected block input | Model contains a block with an unconnected input. |
| Unconnected block output | Model contains a block with an unconnected output. |
| Unconnected line | Model contains an unconnected line. |
| Unneeded type conversions | A Data Type Conversion block is used where no type conversion is necessary. |
| Vector/Matrix conversion | A vector-to-matrix or matrix-to-vector conversion occurred at a block input (see "Vector or Matrix Input Conversion Rules" on page 4–35). |

# The Advanced Pane

The **Advanced** pane allows you to set various options that affect simulation performance.

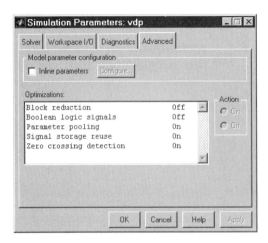

## Model parameter configuration

**Inline parameters.** By default you can modify ("tune") many block parameters during simulation (see "Tunable Parameters" on page 3–5). Selecting this option makes all parameters nontunable except those that you specify. Making parameters nontunable enables Simulink to treat them as constants, thereby speeding up simulation. Using the **Model Parameter Configuration** dialog box (see "Model Parameter Configuration Dialog Box" on page 5-31) to specify the parameters you want to remain tunable when this option is selected. To display the dialog, select the adjacent **Configure** button.

When this option is selected, the only parameters that you can change during simulation are parameters that meet the following conditions:

- The value of the parameter must be a variable defined in the MATLAB workspace.
- The parameter must be specified as global (tunable) in the **Model Parameter Configuration** dialog box.

To tune a parameter that meets these conditions, change the value of the corresponding workspace variable and choose **Update Diagram (Ctrl+D)** from the Simulink **Edit** menu.

If you select this option, Simulink moves constant signals out of the simulation loop. This speeds up the simulation.

## Optimizations

**Block reduction.**  Replaces a group of blocks with a synthesized block, thereby speeding up execution of the model.

**Boolean logic signals.**  Causes blocks that accept Boolean signals to require Boolean signals. If this option is off, blocks that accept inputs of type `boolean` also accept inputs of type `double`. For example, consider the following model.

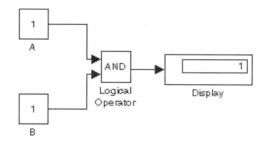

This model connects signals of type `double` to a Logical Operator block, which accepts inputs of type `boolean`. If **Boolean logic signals** option is on, this model generates an error when executed. If **Boolean logic signals** option is off, this model runs without error.

---

**Note**  This option allows the current version of Simulink to run models that were created by earlier versions of Simulink that supported only signals of type `double`.

---

**Parameter pooling.**  This option is used for code generation (see the Real-Time Workshop documentation for more information). Leave this option on if you are not doing code generation.

**Signal storage reuse.** Causes Simulink to reuse memory buffers allocated to store block input and output signals. If this option is off, Simulink allocates a separate memory buffer for each block's outputs. This can substantially increase the amount of memory required to simulate large models. So you should select this option only when you need to debug a model. In particular, you should disable signal storage reuse if you need to:

- Debug a C-MEX S-function
- Use a floating Scope or Display block to inspect signals in a model that you are debugging

  Simulink opens an error dialog if **Signal storage reuse** is enabled and you attempt to use a floating Scope or Display block to display a signal whose buffer has been reused.

**Zero-crossing detection.** Enables zero crossing detection during variable-step simulation of the model. For most models, this speeds up simulation by enabling the solver to take larger time steps. If a model has extreme dynamic changes, disabling this option can speed up the simulation but can also decrease the accuracy of simulation results. See "Zero Crossing Detection" on page 3–13 for more information.

## Model Parameter Configuration Dialog Box

The **Model Parameter Configuration** dialog box allows you to override the **Inline parameters** option (see "Model parameter configuration" on page 5–28) for selected parameters.

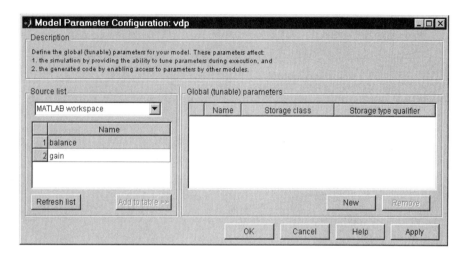

The dialog box has the following controls.

**Source list.**  Displays a list of workspace variables. The options are:

- MATLAB workspace

  List all variables in the MATLAB workspace that have numeric values.

- Referenced workspace variables

  List only those variables referenced by the model.

**Refresh list.**  Updates the source list. Click on this button if you have added a variable to the workspace since the last time the list was displayed.

**Add to table.**  Adds the variable(s) selected in the source list to the adjacent table of tunable parameters.

**New.**  Defines a new parameter and adds it to the list of tunable parameters. Use this button to create tunable parameters that are not yet defined in the MATLAB workspace.

**Note** This option does not create the corresponding variable in the MATLAB workspace. You must create the variable yourself.

**Storage Class.** Used for code generation. See the Real-Time Workshop documentation for more information.

**Storage type qualifier.** Used for code generation. See the Real-Time Workshop documentation for more information.

# Improving Simulation Performance and Accuracy

Simulation performance and accuracy can be affected by many things, including the model design and choice of simulation parameters.

The solvers handle most model simulations accurately and efficiently with their default parameter values. However, some models will yield better results if you adjust solver and simulation parameters. Also, if you know information about your model's behavior, your simulation results can be improved if you provide this information to the solver.

## Speeding Up the Simulation

Slow simulation speed can have many causes. Here are a few:

- Your model includes a MATLAB Fcn block. When a model includes a MATLAB Fcn block, the MATLAB interpreter is called at each time step, drastically slowing down the simulation. Use the built-in Fcn block or Math Function block whenever possible.

- Your model includes an M-file S-function. M-file S-functions also cause the MATLAB interpreter to be called at each time step. Consider either converting the S-function to a subsystem or to a C-MEX file S-function.

- Your model includes a Memory block. Using a Memory block causes the variable-order solvers (ode15s and ode113) to be reset back to order 1 at each time step.

- The maximum step size is too small. If you changed the maximum step size, try running the simulation again with the default value (auto).

- Did you ask for too much accuracy? The default relative tolerance (0.1% accuracy) is usually sufficient. For models with states that go to zero, if the absolute tolerance parameter is too small, the simulation may take too many steps around the near-zero state values. See the discussion of error in "Error Tolerances" on page 5-12.

- The time scale may be too long. Reduce the time interval.

- The problem may be stiff but you're using a nonstiff solver. Try using ode15s.

- The model uses sample times that are not multiples of each other. Mixing sample times that are not multiples of each other causes the solver to take small enough steps to ensure sample time hits for all sample times.

- The model contains an algebraic loop. The solutions to algebraic loops are iteratively computed at every time step. Therefore, they severely degrade performance. For more information, see "Algebraic Loops" on page 3-17.
- Your model feeds a Random Number block into an Integrator block. For continuous systems, use the Band-Limited White Noise block in the Sources library.

## Improving Simulation Accuracy

To check your simulation accuracy, run the simulation over a reasonable time span. Then, reduce either the relative tolerance to 1e-4 (the default is 1e-3) or the absolute tolerance and run it again. Compare the results of both simulations. If the results are not significantly different, you can feel confident that the solution has converged.

If the simulation misses significant behavior at its start, reduce the initial step size to ensure that the simulation does not "step over" the significant behavior.

If the simulation results become unstable over time:

- Your system may be unstable.
- If you are using ode15s, you may need to restrict the maximum order to 2 (the maximum order for which the solver is A-stable) or try using the ode23s solver.

If the simulation results do not appear to be accurate:

- For a model that has states whose values approach zero, if the absolute tolerance parameter is too large, the simulation will take too few steps around areas of near-zero state values. Reduce this parameter value or adjust it for individual states in the Integrator dialog box.
- If reducing the absolute tolerances do not sufficiently improve the accuracy, reduce the size of the relative tolerance parameter to reduce the acceptable error and force smaller step sizes and more steps.

**6**

# Analyzing Simulation Results

# Viewing Output Trajectories

Output trajectories from Simulink can be plotted using one of three methods:

- Feeding a signal into either a Scope or an XY Graph block
- Writing output to return variables and using MATLAB plotting commands
- Writing output to the workspace using To Workspace blocks and plotting the results using MATLAB plotting commands

## Using the Scope Block

You can use display output trajectories on a Scope block during a simulation. This simple model shows an example of the use of the Scope block.

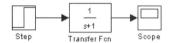

The display on the Scope shows the output trajectory. The Scope block enables you to zoom in on an area of interest or save the data to the workspace.

The XY Graph block enables you to plot one signal against another.

These blocks are described in the "Block Reference" in the online Simulink help.

## Using Return Variables

By returning time and output histories, you can use MATLAB plotting commands to display and annotate the output trajectories.

The block labeled Out is an Outport block from the Signals & Systems library. The output trajectory, yout, is returned by the integration solver. For more information, see "The Workspace I/O Pane" on page 5-17.

You can also run this simulation from the **Simulation** menu by specifying variables for the time, output, and states on the **Workspace I/O** page of the **Simulation Parameters** dialog box. You can then plot these results using

```
plot(tout,yout)
```

## Using the To Workspace Block

The To Workspace block can be used to return output trajectories to the MATLAB workspace. The model below illustrates this use.

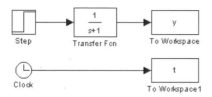

The variables y and t appear in the workspace when the simulation is complete. The time vector is stored by feeding a Clock block into a To Workspace block. The time vector can also be acquired by entering a variable name for the time on the **Workspace I/O** pane of the **Simulation Parameters** dialog box for menu-driven simulations, or by returning it using the sim command (see "The Workspace I/O Pane" on page 5-17 for more information).

The To Workspace block can accept an array input, with each input element's trajectory stored in the resulting workspace variable.

# Linearization

Simulink provides the `linmod` and `dlinmod` functions to extract linear models in the form of the state-space matrices $A$, $B$, $C$, and $D$. State-space matrices describe the linear input-output relationship as

$$\dot{x} = Ax + Bu$$
$$y = Cx + Du$$

where $x$, $u$, and $y$ are state, input, and output vectors, respectively. For example, the following model is called `lmod`.

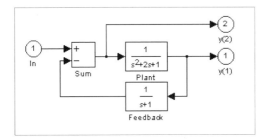

To extract the linear model of this Simulink system, enter this command.

```
[A,B,C,D] = linmod('lmod')
A =
     -2     -1     -1
      1      0      0
      0      1     -1
B =
      1
      0
      0
C =
      0      1      0
      0      0     -1
D =
      0
      1
```

Inputs and outputs must be defined using Inport and Outport blocks from the Signals & Systems library. Source and sink blocks do not act as inputs and outputs. Inport blocks can be used in conjunction with source blocks using a Sum block. Once the data is in the state-space form or converted to an LTI object, you can apply functions in the Control System Toolbox for further analysis:

- Conversion to an LTI object

```
sys = ss(A,B,C,D);
```

- Bode phase and magnitude frequency plot

```
bode(A,B,C,D) or bode(sys)
```

- Linearized time response

```
step(A,B,C,D) or step(sys)
impulse(A,B,C,D) or impulse(sys)
lsim(A,B,C,D,u,t) or lsim(sys,u,t)
```

Other functions in the Control System Toolbox and Robust Control Toolbox can be used for linear control system design.

When the model is nonlinear, an operating point may be chosen at which to extract the linearized model. The nonlinear model is also sensitive to the perturbation sizes at which the model is extracted. These must be selected to balance the trade-off between truncation and roundoff error. Extra arguments to linmod specify the operating point and perturbation points.

```
[A,B,C,D] = linmod('sys', x, u, pert, xpert, upert)
```

For discrete systems or mixed continuous and discrete systems, use the function dlinmod for linearization. This has the same calling syntax as linmod except that the second right-hand argument must contain a sample time at which to perform the linearization. For more information, see linfun in the online Simulink help.

Using linmod to linearize a model that contains Derivative or Transport Delay blocks can be troublesome. Before linearizing, replace these blocks with specially designed blocks that avoid the problems. These blocks are in the Simulink Extras library in the Linearization sublibrary. You access the Extras library by opening the Blocksets & Toolboxes icon:

- For the Derivative block, use the Switched derivative for linearization.

- For the Transport Delay block, use the Switched transport delay for linearization. (Using this block requires that you have the Control System Toolbox.)

When using a Derivative block, you can also try to incorporate the derivative term in other blocks. For example, if you have a Derivative block in series with a Transfer Fcn block, it is better implemented (although this is not always possible) with a single Transfer Fcn block of the form

$$\frac{s}{s + a}$$

In this example, the blocks on the left of this figure can be replaced by the block on the right.

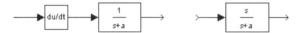

# Equilibrium Point Determination

The Simulink `trim` function determines steady-state equilibrium points. Consider, for example, this model, called `lmod`.

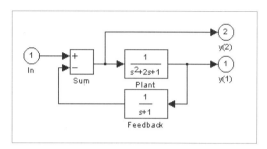

You can use the `trim` function to find the values of the input and the states that set both outputs to 1. First, make initial guesses for the state variables (x) and input values (u), then set the desired value for the output (y).

```
x = [0; 0; 0];
u = 0;
y = [1; 1];
```

Use index variables to indicate which variables are fixed and which can vary.

```
ix = [];      % Don't fix any of the states
iu = [];      % Don't fix the input
iy = [1;2];   % Fix both output 1 and output 2
```

Invoking `trim` returns the solution. Your results may differ due to roundoff error.

```
[x,u,y,dx] = trim('lmod',x,u,y,ix,iu,iy)

x =
    0.0000
    1.0000
    1.0000
u =
    2
y =
    1.0000
    1.0000
dx =
    1.0e-015 *
    -0.2220
    -0.0227
     0.3331
```

Note that there may be no solution to equilibrium point problems. If that is the case, `trim` returns a solution that minimizes the maximum deviation from the desired result after first trying to set the derivatives to zero. For a description of the `trim` syntax, see `trim` in the Simulink online help.

# Using Masks to Customize Blocks

# Introduction

Masking is a powerful Simulink feature that enables you to customize the dialog box and icon for a subsystem. With masking, you can:

- Simplify the use of your model by replacing many dialog boxes in a subsystem with a single one. Instead of requiring the user of the model to open each block and enter parameter values, those parameter values can be entered on the mask dialog box and passed to the blocks in the masked subsystem.

- Provide a more descriptive and helpful user interface by defining a dialog box with your own block description, parameter field labels, and help text.

- Define commands that compute variables whose values depend on block parameters.

- Create a block icon that depicts the subsystem's purpose.

- Prevent unintended modification of subsystems by hiding their contents behind a customized interface.

- Create dynamic dialogs.

# A Sample Masked Subsystem

This simple subsystem models the equation for a line, y = mx + b.

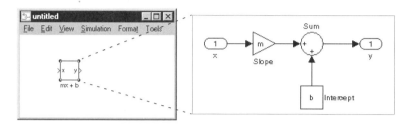

Ordinarily, when you double-click on a Subsystem block, the Subsystem block opens, displaying its blocks in a separate window. The mx + b subsystem contains a Gain block, named Slope, whose Gain parameter is specified as m, and a Constant block, named Intercept, whose Constant value parameter is specified as b. These parameters represent the slope and intercept of a line.

This example creates a custom dialog box and icon for the subsystem. One dialog box contains prompts for both the slope and the intercept. After you create the mask, double-click on the Subsystem block to open the mask dialog box. The mask dialog box and icon look like this.

The mask dialog box

The block icon

A user enters values for **Slope** and **Intercept** into the mask dialog box. Simulink makes these values available to all the blocks in the underlying subsystem. Masking this subsystem creates a self-contained functional unit with its own application-specific parameters, Slope and Intercept. The mask maps these *mask parameters* to the generic parameters of the underlying blocks. The complexity of the subsystem is encapsulated by a new interface that has the look and feel of a built-in Simulink block.

To create a mask for this subsystem, you need to:

- Specify the prompts for the mask dialog box parameters. In this example, the mask dialog box has prompts for the slope and intercept.
- Specify the variable name used to store the value of each parameter.
- Enter the documentation of the block, consisting of the block description and the block help text.
- Specify the drawing command that creates the block icon.
- Specify the commands that provide the variables needed by the drawing command (there are none in this example).

## Creating Mask Dialog Box Prompts

To create the mask for this subsystem, select the Subsystem block and choose **Mask Subsystem** from the **Edit** menu.

The mask dialog box shown at the beginning of this section is created largely on the **Initialization** pane of the Mask Editor. For this sample model, the pane looks like this.

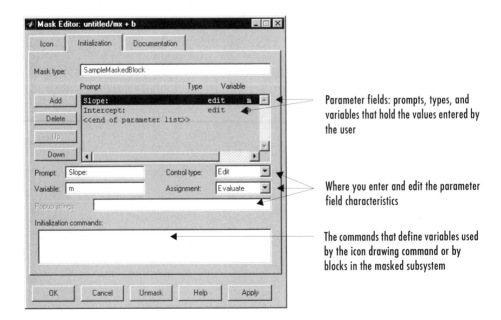

Parameter fields: prompts, types, and variables that hold the values entered by the user

Where you enter and edit the parameter field characteristics

The commands that define variables used by the icon drawing command or by blocks in the masked subsystem

The Mask Editor enables you to specify these attributes of a mask parameter:

- The prompt – the text label that describes the parameter
- The control type – the style of user interface control that determines how parameter values are entered or selected
- The variable – the name of the variable that will store the parameter value

Generally, it is convenient to refer to masked parameters by their prompts. In this example, the parameter associated with slope is referred to as the Slope parameter, and the parameter associated with intercept is referred to as the Intercept parameter.

The slope and intercept are defined as edit controls. This means that the user types values into edit fields in the mask dialog box. These values are stored in variables in the *mask workspace*. Masked blocks can access variables only in the mask workspace. In this example, the value entered for the slope is assigned to the variable m. The Slope block in the masked subsystem gets the value for the slope parameter from the mask workspace. This figure shows how the slope parameter definitions in the Mask Editor map to the actual mask dialog box parameters.

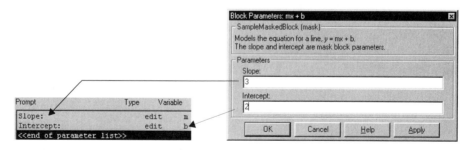

After you have created the mask parameters for slope and intercept, press the **OK** button. Then, double-click on the Subsystem block to open the newly constructed dialog box. Enter 3 for the **Slope** and 2 for the **Intercept** parameter.

## Creating the Block Description and Help Text

The mask type, block description, and help text are defined on the
**Documentation** pane. For this sample masked block, the pane looks like this.

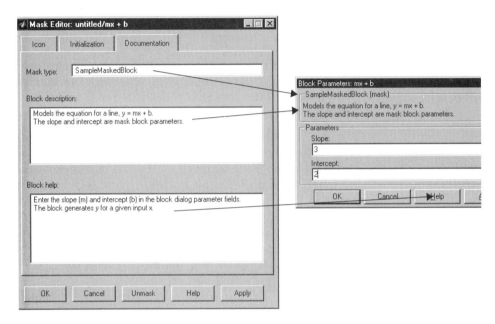

## Creating the Block Icon

So far, we have created a customized dialog box for the mx + b subsystem.
However, the Subsystem block still displays the generic Simulink subsystem
icon. An appropriate icon for this masked block is a plot that indicates the slope
of the line. For a slope of 3, that icon looks like this.

The block icon is defined on the **Icon** pane. For this block, the **Icon** pane looks like this.

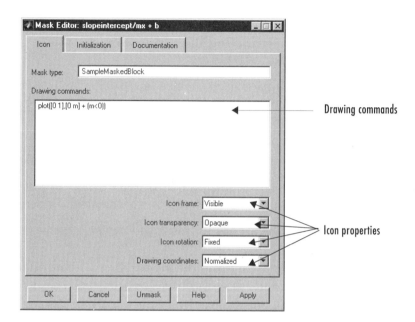

The drawing command plots a line from (0,0) to (1,m). If the slope is negative, Simulink shifts the line up by 1 to keep it within the visible drawing area of the block.

The drawing commands have access to all of the variables in the mask workspace. As you enter different values of slope, the icon updates the slope of the plotted line.

Select **Normalized** as the **Drawing coordinates** parameter, located at the bottom of the list of icon properties, to specify that the icon be drawn in a frame whose bottom-left corner is (0,0) and whose top-right corner is (1,1). See "Displaying Graphics on the Block Icon" on page 7-19 for more information.

# The Mask Editor: An Overview

To mask a subsystem (you can only mask Subsystem blocks), select the Subsystem block, then choose **Mask Subsystem** from the **Edit** menu. The Mask Editor appears. The Mask Editor consists of three panes, each handling a different aspect of the mask:

- The **Initialization** pane enables you to define and describe mask dialog box parameter prompts, name the variables associated with the parameters, and specify initialization commands.
- The **Icon** pane enables you to define the block icon.
- The **Documentation** pane enables you to define the mask type and specify the block description and the block help.

Five buttons appear along the bottom of the Mask Editor:

- The **OK** button applies the mask settings on all panes and closes the Mask Editor.
- The **Cancel** button closes the Mask Editor without applying any changes made since you last pressed the **Apply** button.
- The **Unmask** button deactivates the mask and closes the Mask Editor. The mask information is retained so that the mask can be reactivated. To reactivate the mask, select the block and choose **Create Mask**. The Mask Editor opens, displaying the previous settings. The inactive mask information is discarded when the model is closed and cannot be recovered.
- The **Help** button displays the contents of this chapter.
- The **Apply** button creates or changes the mask using the information that appears on all masking panes. The Mask Editor remains open.

To see the system under the mask without unmasking it, select the Subsystem block, then choose **Look Under Mask** from the **Edit** menu. This command opens the subsystem. The block's mask is not affected.

# The Initialization Pane

The mask interface enables a user of a masked system to enter parameter values for blocks within the masked system. You create the mask interface by defining prompts for parameter values on the **Initialization** pane. The **Initialization** pane for the mx+b sample masked system looks like this.

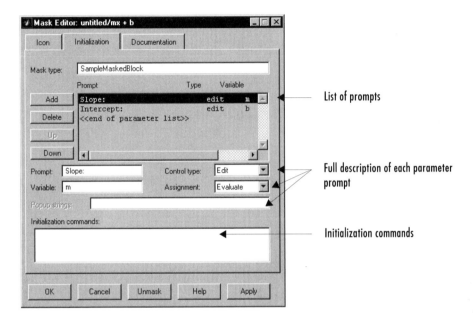

List of prompts

Full description of each parameter prompt

Initialization commands

## Prompts and Associated Variables

A *prompt* provides information that helps the user enter or select a value for a block parameter. Prompts appear on the mask dialog box in the order they appear in the **Prompt** list.

When you define a prompt, you also specify the variable that is to store the parameter value, choose the style of control for the prompt, and indicate how the value is to be stored in the variable.

If the **Assignment** type is **Evaluate**, the value entered by the user is evaluated by MATLAB before it is assigned to the variable. If the type is **Literal**, the value entered by the user is not evaluated, but is assigned to the variable as a string.

For example, if the user enters the string gain in an edit field and the **Assignment** type is **Evaluate**, the string gain is evaluated by MATLAB and the result is assigned to the variable. If the type is **Literal**, the string is not evaluated by MATLAB so the variable contains the string 'gain'.

If you need both the string entered as well as the evaluated value, choose **Literal**. Then use the MATLAB eval command in the initialization commands. For example, if LitVal is the string 'gain', then to obtain the evaluated value, use the command

```
value = eval(LitVal)
```

In general, most parameters use an **Assignment** type of **Evaluate**.

### Creating the First Prompt

To create the first prompt in the list, enter the prompt in the **Prompt** field, the variable that is to contain the parameter value in the **Variable** field, and choose a control style and an assignment type.

### Inserting a Prompt

To insert a prompt in the list:

**1** Select the prompt that appears immediately *below* where you want to insert the new prompt and click on the **Add** button to the left of the prompt list.

**2** Enter the text for the prompt in the **Prompt** field. Enter the variable that is to hold the parameter value in the **Variable** field.

### Editing a Prompt

To edit an existing prompt:

**1** Select the prompt in the list. The prompt, variable name, control style, and assignment type appear in the fields below the list.

**2** Edit the appropriate value. When you click the mouse outside the field or press the **Enter** or **Return** key, Simulink updates the prompt.

### Deleting a Prompt

To delete a prompt from the list:

**1** Select the prompt you want to delete.

**2** Click on the **Delete** button to the left of the prompt list.

### Moving a Prompt

To move a prompt in the list:

**1** Select the prompt you want to move.

**2** To move the prompt up one position in the prompt list, click on the **Up** button to the left of the prompt list. To move the prompt down one position, click on the **Down** button.

## Control Types

Simulink enables you to choose how parameter values are entered or selected. You can create three styles of controls: edit fields, check boxes, and pop-up controls. For example, this figure shows the parameter area of a mask dialog box which uses all three styles of controls (with the pop-up control open).

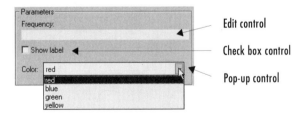

### Defining an Edit Control

An *edit field* enables the user to enter a parameter value by typing it into a field. This figure shows how the prompt for the sample edit control was defined.

The value of the variable associated with the parameter (freq) is determined by the **Assignment** type defined for the prompt.

| Assignment | Value |
|------------|-------|
| Evaluate | The result of evaluating the expression entered in the field. |
| Literal | The actual string entered in the field. |

### Defining a Check Box Control

A *check box* enables the user to choose between two alternatives by selecting or deselecting a check box. This figure shows how the sample check box control is defined.

The value of the variable associated with the parameter (label) depends on whether the check box is selected and the **Assignment** type defined for the prompt.

| Check Box | Evaluated Value | Literal Value |
|-----------|-----------------|---------------|
| Checked | 1 | 'on' |
| Not checked | 0 | 'off' |

### Defining a Pop-Up Control

A *popup* enables the user to choose a parameter value from a list of possible values. You specify the list in the **Popup strings** field, separating items with a vertical line ( | ). This figure shows how the sample pop-up control is defined.

The value of the variable associated with the parameter (color) depends on the item selected from the pop-up list and the **Assignment** type defined for the prompt.

| Assignment | Value |
|------------|-------|
| Evaluate | The index of the value selected from the list, starting with 1. For example, if the third item is selected, the parameter value is 3. |
| Literal | A string that is the value selected. If the third item is selected, the parameter value is 'green'. |

## Default Values for Masked Block Parameters

To change default parameter values in a masked library block, follow these steps:

**1** Unlock the library.

**2** Open the block to access its dialog box, fill in the desired default values, and close the dialog box.

**3** Save the library.

When the block is copied into a model and opened, the default values appear on the block's dialog box.

For more information, see "Libraries" on page 4–57.

## Tunable Parameters

A tunable parameter is a parameter that a user can modify at runtime. When you create a mask, all its parameters are tunable. You can subsequently disable or re-enable tuning of any of a mask's parameters via the MaskTunableValues parameter. The value of this parameter is a cell array of strings, each of which corresponds to one of a masked block's parameters. The first cell corresponds to the first parameter, the second cell to the second parameter, and so on. If a parameter is tunable, the value of the corresponding cell is on; otherwise, the value is off. To enable or disable tuning of a parameter, first get the cell array, using get_param. Then, set the corresponding cell to on or off and reset the MaskTunableValues parameter using set_param. For example, the following commands disable tuning of the first parameter of the currently selected masked block.

```
ca = get_param(gcb, 'MaskTunableValues');
ca(1) = 'off'
set_param(gcb, 'MaskTunableValues', ca)
```

After changing a block's tunable parameters, make the changes permanent by saving the block.

## Initialization Commands

Initialization commands define variables that reside in the mask workspace. These variables can be used by all initialization commands defined for the mask, by blocks in the masked subsystem, and by commands that draw the block icon (drawing commands).

Simulink executes the initialization commands when:

• The model is loaded.

• The simulation is started or the block diagram is updated.

• The masked block is rotated.

• The block's icon needs to be redrawn and the plot commands depend on variables defined in the initialization commands.

Initialization commands are valid MATLAB expressions, consisting of MATLAB functions, operators, and variables defined in the mask workspace. Initialization commands cannot access base workspace variables. Terminate initialization commands with a semicolon to avoid echoing results to the command window.

### The Mask Workspace

Simulink creates a local workspace, called a *mask workspace*, when either of the following occurs:

• The mask contains initialization commands.

• The mask defines prompts and associates variables with those prompts.

The contents of a mask workspace include the variables associated with the mask's parameters and variables defined by initialization commands.

In the mx + b example, described earlier in this chapter, the Mask Editor explicitly creates m and b in the mask workspace by associating a variable with a mask parameter. The figure below shows the mapping of values entered in the mask dialog box to variables in the mask workspace (indicated by the solid line) and the access of those variables by the underlying blocks (indicated by the dashed line).

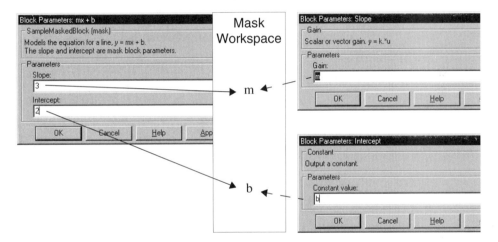

Mask workspaces are analogous to the local workspaces used by M-file functions. You can think of the expressions entered into the dialog boxes of the underlying blocks and the initialization commands entered on the Mask Editor as lines of an M-file function. Using this analogy, the local workspace for this "function" is the mask workspace.

Masked subsystems create a hierarchy of workspaces. The workspace of a masked block is a subspace of the model workspace and of the workspaces of any blocks that contain the masked block. A masked block can access all variables that are uniquely defined in its workspace hierarchy. The blocks in a masked subsystem can similarly access any uniquely defined variable in the masked subsystem's workspace hierarchy.

If a variable is defined in more than one place in the hierarchy, the masked block can access only the most local definition. For example, suppose that model M contains masked subsystem A, which contains masked subsystem B.

Further suppose that B refers to a variable x that exists in both A's and M's workspaces. In this case, the reference resolves to the value of x in A's workspace.

---

**Note** A masked block's initialization code can access only variables defined in the masked block's local workspace.

---

### Debugging Initialization Commands

You can debug initialization commands in these ways:

- Specify an initialization command without a terminating semicolon to echo its results to the command window.
- Place a keyboard command in the initialization commands to stop execution and give control to the keyboard. For more information, see the help text for the keyboard command.
- Enter either of these commands in the MATLAB command window.

```
dbstop if error
dbstop if warning
```

If an error occurs in the initialization commands, execution stops and you can examine the mask workspace. For more information, see the help text for the dbstop command.

# The Icon Pane

The **Icon** pane enables you to customize the masked block's icon. You create a custom icon by specifying commands in the **Drawing commands** field. You can create icons that show descriptive text, state equations, images, and graphics. This figure shows the **Icon** pane.

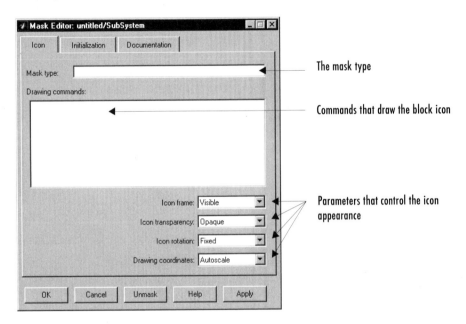

Drawing commands have access to all variables in the mask workspace.

Drawing commands can display text, one or more plots, or show a transfer function. If you enter more than one command, the results of the commands are drawn on the icon in the order the commands appear.

## Displaying Text on the Block Icon

To display text on the icon, enter one of these drawing commands.

```
disp('text') or disp(variablename)
```

```
text(x, y, 'text')
text(x, y, stringvariablename)
```

```
text(x, y, text, 'horizontalAlignment', halign,
'verticalAlignment', valign)
```

```
fprintf('text') or fprintf('format', variablename)
```

```
port_label(port_type, port_number, label)
```

The disp command displays text or the contents of variablename centered on the icon.

The text command places a character string (text or the contents of stringvariablename) at a location specified by the point (x,y). The units depend on the **Drawing coordinates** parameter. For more information, see "Controlling Icon Properties" on page 7–22.

You can optionally specify the horizontal and/or vertical alignment of the text relative to the point (x, y) in the text command. For example, the command

```
text(0.5, 0.5, 'foobar', 'horizontalAlignment', 'center')
```

centers foobar in the icon.

The text command offers the following horizontal alignment options.

| Option | Aligns |
| --- | --- |
| left | The left end of the text at the specified point |
| right | The right end of the text at the specified point |
| center | The center of the text at the specified point |

The text command offers the following vertical alignment options.

| Option | Aligns |
| --- | --- |
| base | The baseline of the text at the specified point |
| bottom | The bottom line of the text at the specified point |
| middle | The midline of the text at the specified point |

| Option | Aligns |
|--------|--------|
| cap | The capitals line of the text at the specified point |
| top | The top of the text at the specified point |

The fprintf command displays formatted text centered on the icon and can display text along with the contents of variablename.

---

**Note** While these commands are identical in name to their corresponding MATLAB functions, they provide only the functionality described above.

---

To display more than one line of text, use \n to indicate a line break. For example, the figure below shows two samples of the disp command.

The port_label command lets you specify the labels of ports displayed on the icon. The command's syntax is

```
port_label(port_type, port_number, label)
```

where port_type is either 'input' or 'output', port_number is an integer, and label is a string specifying the port's label. For example, the command

```
port_label('input', 1, 'a')
```

defines a as the label of input port 1.

## Displaying Graphics on the Block Icon

You can display plots on your masked block icon by entering one or more plot commands. You can use these forms of the plot command.

```
plot(Y);
plot(X1,Y1,X2,Y2,...);
```

plot(Y) plots, for a vector Y, each element against its index. If Y is a matrix, it plots each column of the matrix as though it were a vector.

plot(X1,Y1,X2,Y2,...) plots the vectors Y1 against X1, Y2 against X2, and so on. Vector pairs must be the same length and the list must consist of an even number of vectors.

For example, this command generates the plot that appears on the icon for the Ramp block, in the Sources library. The icon appears below the command.

    plot([0 1 5], [0 0 4])

Ramp

Plot commands can include NaN and inf values. When NaNs or infs are encountered, Simulink stops drawing, then begins redrawing at the next numbers that are not NaN or inf.

The appearance of the plot on the icon depends on the value of the **Drawing coordinates** parameter. For more information, see "Controlling Icon Properties" on page 7–22.

Simulink displays three question marks (? ? ?) in the block icon and issues warnings in these situations:

- When the values for the parameters used in the drawing commands are not yet defined (for example, when the mask is first created and values have not yet been entered into the mask dialog box)
- When a masked block parameter or drawing command is entered incorrectly

## Displaying Images on Masks

The masked dialog functions, image and patch, enable you to display bitmapped images and draw patches on masked block icons.

image(a) displays the image a where a is an M-by-N-by-3 array of RGB values. You can use the MATLAB commands, imread and ind2rgb, to read and convert bitmap files to the necessary matrix format. For example,

    image(imread('icon.tif'))

reads the icon image from a TIFF file named icon.tif in the MATLAB path.

image(a, [x, y, w, h]) creates the image at the specified position relative to the lower left corner of the mask.

image(a, [x, y, w, h], rotation) allows you to specify whether the image rotates ('on') or remains stationary ('off') as the icon rotates. The default is 'off'.

patch(x, y) creates a solid patch having the shape specified by the coordinate vectors x and y. The patch's color is the current foreground color.

patch(x, y, [r g b]) creates a solid patch of the color specified by the vector [r g b], where r is the red component, g the green, and b the blue. For example,

```
patch([0 .5 1], [0 1 0], [1 0 0])
```

creates a red triangle on the mask's icon.

## Displaying a Transfer Function on the Block Icon

To display a transfer function equation in the block icon, enter the following command in the **Drawing commands** field.

```
dpoly(num, den)
dpoly(num, den, 'character')
```

num and den are vectors of transfer function numerator and denominator coefficients, typically defined using initialization commands. The equation is expressed in terms of the specified character. The default is s. When the icon is drawn, the initialization commands are executed and the resulting equation is drawn on the icon:

- To display a continuous transfer function in descending powers of s, enter

```
dpoly(num, den)
```

For example, for num = [0 0 1]; and den = [1 2 1]; the icon looks like this.

$$\frac{1}{s^2+2s+1}$$

- To display a discrete transfer function in descending powers of $z$, enter

  dpoly(num, den, 'z')

  For example, for num = [0 0 1]; and den = [1 2 1]; the icon looks like this.

  $$\frac{1}{z^2+2z+1}$$

- To display a discrete transfer function in ascending powers of $1/z$, enter

  dpoly(num, den, 'z-')

  For example, for num and den as defined above, the icon looks like this.

  $$\frac{z^{-2}}{1+2z^{-1}+z^{-2}}$$

- To display a zero-pole gain transfer function, enter

  droots(z, p, k)

  For example, the above command creates this icon for these values.

  z = []; p = [-1 -1]; k = 1;

  $$\frac{1}{(s+1)(s+1)}$$

  You can add a fourth argument ('z' or 'z-') to express the equation in terms of $z$ or $1/z$.

If the parameters are not defined or have no values when you create the icon, Simulink displays three question marks (? ? ?) in the icon. When the parameter values are entered in the mask dialog box, Simulink evaluates the transfer function and displays the resulting equation in the icon.

## Controlling Icon Properties

You can control a masked block's icon properties by selecting among the choices below the **Drawing commands** field.

### Icon frame

The icon frame is the rectangle that encloses the block. You can choose to show or hide the frame by setting the **Icon frame** parameter to **Visible** or **Invisible**.

The default is to make the icon frame visible. For example, this figure shows visible and invisible icon frames for an AND gate block.

Visible                    Invisible

### Icon transparency

The icon can be set to **Opaque** or **Transparent**, either hiding or showing what is underneath the icon. **Opaque**, the default, covers information Simulink draws, such as port labels. This figure shows opaque and transparent icons for an AND gate block. Notice the text on the transparent icon.

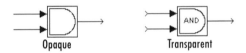

Opaque                    Transparent

### Icon rotation

When the block is rotated or flipped, you can choose whether to rotate or flip the icon, or to have it remain fixed in its original orientation. The default is not to rotate the icon. The icon rotation is consistent with block port rotation. This figure shows the results of choosing **Fixed** and **Rotates** icon rotation when the AND gate block is rotated.

Fixed        Rotates

### Drawing coordinates

This parameter controls the coordinate system used by the drawing commands. This parameter applies only to plot and text drawing commands. You can select from among these choices: **Autoscale**, **Normalized**, and **Pixel**.

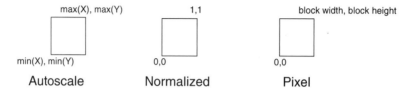

Autoscale          Normalized          Pixel

- **Autoscale** automatically scales the icon within the block frame. When the block is resized, the icon is also resized. For example, this figure shows the icon drawn using these vectors.

  ```
  X = [0 2 3 4 9]; Y = [4 6 3 5 8];
  ```

  The lower-left corner of the block frame is (0,3) and the upper-right corner is (9,8). The range of the *x*-axis is 9 (from 0 to 9), while the range of the *y*-axis is 5 (from 3 to 8).

- **Normalized** draws the icon within a block frame whose bottom-left corner is (0,0) and whose top right corner is (1,1). Only X and Y values between 0 and 1 appear. When the block is resized, the icon is also resized. For example, this figure shows the icon drawn using these vectors.

  ```
  X = [.0 .2 .3 .4 .9]; Y = [.4 .6 .3 .5 .8];
  ```

- **Pixel** draws the icon with X and Y values expressed in pixels. The icon is not automatically resized when the block is resized. To force the icon to resize with the block, define the drawing commands in terms of the block size.

  This example demonstrates how to create an improved icon for the mx + b sample masked subsystem discussed earlier in this chapter. These initialization commands define the data that enables the drawing command to produce an accurate icon regardless of the shape of the block.

```
pos = get_param(gcb, 'Position');
width = pos(3) − pos(1); height = pos(4) − pos(2);
x = [0, width];
if (m >= 0), y = [0, (m*width)]; end
if (m < 0),  y = [height, (height + (m*width))]; end
```

The drawing command that generates this icon is plot(x,y).

# The Documentation Pane

The **Documentation** pane enables you to define or modify the type, description, and help text for a masked block. This figure shows how fields on the **Documentation** pane correspond to the mx+b sample mask block's dialog box.

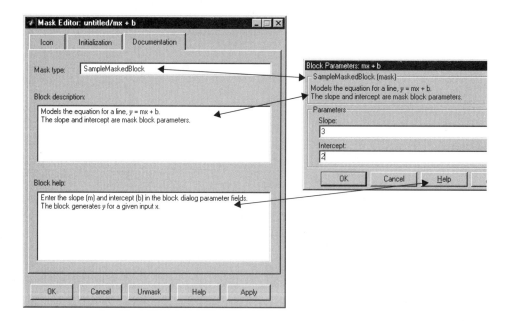

## The Mask Type Field

The mask type is a block classification used only for purposes of documentation. It appears in the block's dialog box and on all Mask Editor panes for the block. You can choose any name you want for the mask type. When Simulink creates the block's dialog box, it adds "(mask)" after the mask type to differentiate masked blocks from built-in blocks.

## The Block Description Field

The block description is informative text that appears in the block's dialog box in the frame under the mask type. If you are designing a system for others to use, this is a good place to describe the block's purpose or function.

Simulink automatically wraps long lines of text. You can force line breaks by using the **Enter** or **Return** key.

## The Block Help Field

You can provide help text that gets displayed when the **Help** button is pressed on the masked block's dialog box. If you create models for others to use, this is a good place to explain how the block works and how to enter its parameters.

You can include user-written documentation for a masked block's help. You can specify any of the following for the masked block help text:

- URL specification (a string starting with `http:`, `www`, `file:`, `ftp:`, or `mailto:`)
- `web` command (launches a browser)
- `eval` command (evaluates a MATLAB string)
- Static text displayed in the Web browser

Simulink examines the first line of the masked block help text. If it detects a URL specification, `web` command, or `eval` command, it accesses the block help as directed; otherwise, the full contents of the masked block help text are displayed in the browser.

These examples illustrate several acceptable commands.

```
web([docroot '/My Blockset Doc/' get_param(gcb,'MaskType')...
'.html'])
eval('!Word My_Spec.doc')
http://www.mathworks.com
file:///c:/mydir/helpdoc.html
www.mathworks.com
```

Simulink automatically wraps long lines of text.

# Creating Self-Modifying Masked Blocks

A masked block can modify itself based on user input. In particular, a masked block can change the contents of its underlying system block and set the parameters of those blocks based on user input. For example, you can create a block that adds or deletes input and output ports depending on some user setting.

When creating a self-modifying masked block, you must set its MaskSelfModifiable parameter to 'on'. Otherwise, Simulink generates an error when the block tries to modify itself, that is, when any code in the masked block's workspace tries to add or delete blocks from the underlying system block or modify the parameters of any blocks in the underlying system block.

To set the MaskSelfModifiable parameter, select the self-modifying block and enter the following command

```
set_param(gcb, 'MaskSelfModifiable', 'on');
```

at the MATLAB prompt. Then, save the block.

**8**

# Simulink Debugger

The Simulink debugger is a tool for locating and diagnosing bugs in a Simulink model. It enables you to pinpoint problems by running simulations step-by-step and displaying intermediate block states and input and outputs. The Simulink debugger has both a graphical and a command-line user interface. The graphical interface allows you to access the debugger's most commonly used features. The command-line interface gives you access to all the debugger's capabilities. Wherever you can use either interface to perform a task, the documentation shows you first how to use the graphical interface and then the command-line interface to perform the task.

# Starting the Debugger

To start the debugger, open the model you want to debug and select **Debugger** from the Simulink **Tools** menu. The debugger window appears.

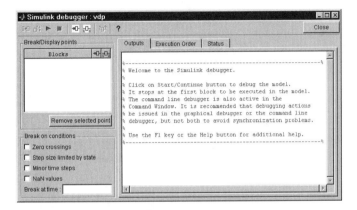

You can also start the debugger from the MATLAB command line, using the `sldebug` command or the debug option of the `sim` command to start a model under debugger control. (See "Running a Simulation from the Command Line" in the online Simulink help for information on specifying `sim` options.) For example, either the command

```
sim('vdp',[0,10],simset('debug','on'))
```

or the command

```
sldebug 'vdp'
```

loads the Simulink demo model, `vdp`, into memory, starts the simulation, and stops the simulation at the first block in the model's execution list.

---

**Note** When running the debugger in Graphical User Interface (GUI) mode, you must explicitly start the simulation. See "Starting the Simulation" on page 8–4 for more information.

---

# Starting the Simulation

To start the simulation, select the **Start/Continue** button in the debugger's toolbar.

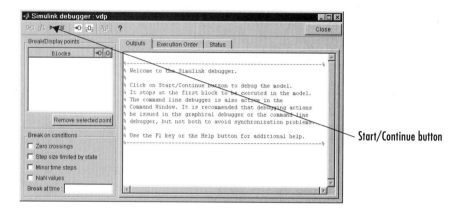

Start/Continue button

The simulation starts and stops at the first block to be executed. The debugger opens the model window's browser pane and highlights the block at which model execution has stopped.

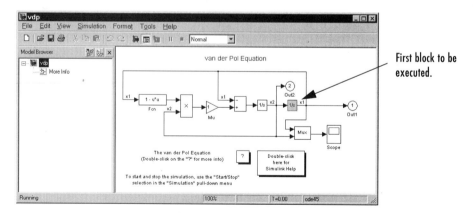

First block to be executed.

The debugger displays the simulation start time and a debug command prompt in the MATLAB command window when the debugger is running in

command-line mode or in the debugger's output pane when the debugger is
running in GUI mode.

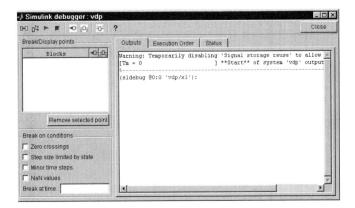

The command prompt displays the block index (see "About Block Indexes" on
page 8–6) and name of the first block to be executed.

---

**Note** When you start the debugger in GUI mode, the debugger's
command-line interface is also active in the MATLAB command window.
However, you should avoid using the command-line interface to prevent
synchronization errors between the graphical and command line interfaces.

---

At this point, you can set breakpoints, run the simulation step-by-step,
continue the simulation to the next breakpoint or end, examine data, or
perform other debugging tasks. The following sections explain how to use the
debugger's graphical controls to perform these debugging tasks.

# Using the Debugger's Command-Line Interface

In command-line mode, you control the debugger by entering commands at the debugger command line in the MATLAB command window. The debugger accepts abbreviations for debugger commands. See "Debugger Command Reference" in the online Simulink help for a list of command abbreviations and repeatable commands. You can repeat some commands by entering an empty command (i.e., by pressing the **Return** key) at the MATLAB command line.

## About Block Indexes

Many Simulink debugger commands and messages use block indexes to refer to blocks. A block index has the form s:b where s is an integer identifying a system in the model being debugged and b is an integer identifying a block within that system. For example, the block index 0:1 refers to block 1 in the model's 0 system. The slist command shows the block index for each block in the model being debugged (see slist in the "Debugger Command Reference" in the online Simulink help).

## Accessing the MATLAB Workspace

You can type any MATLAB expression at the sldebug prompt. For example, suppose you are at a breakpoint and you are logging time and output of your model as tout and yout. Then the following command

```
(sldebug ...) plot(tout, yout)
```

creates a plot. Suppose you would like to access a variable whose name is the same as the complete or incomplete name of an sldebug command, for example, s, which is a partial completion for the step command. Typing an s at the sldebug prompt steps the model. However,

```
(sldebug...) eval('s')
```

displays the value of the variable s.

# Getting Online Help

You can get online help on using the debugger's by selecting the **Help** button on the debugger's toolbar or by pressing the F1 key when the text cursor is in a debugger panel or text field. Pressing the **Help** button displays help for the debugger in the MATLAB Help browser.

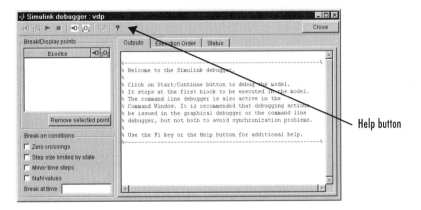

Help button

Pressing the F1 key displays help for the debugger panel or text field that currently has the keyboard input focus. In command-line mode, you can get a brief description of the debugger commands by typing help at the debug prompt.

# Running a Simulation

The Simulink debugger lets you run a simulation from the point at which it is currently suspended to the following points:

- End of the simulation
- Next breakpoint (see "Setting Breakpoints" on page 8–11)
- Next block
- Next time step

You select the amount to advance by selecting the appropriate button on the debugger toolbar in GUI mode

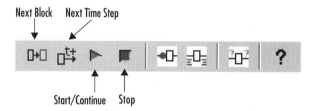

or by entering the appropriate debugger command in command-line mode.

| Command | Advances a Simulation |
|---------|------------------------|
| step | One block |
| next | One time step |
| continue | To next breakpoint |
| run | To end of simulation, ignoring breakpoints |

## Continuing a Simulation

In GUI mode, the debugger colors the **Run/Continue** button red when it has suspended the simulation for any reason. To continue the simulation, select the **Run/Continue** button. In command-line mode, enter continue to continue the simulation. The debugger continues the simulation to the next breakpoint (see

"Setting Breakpoints" on page 8–11) or to the end of the simulation, whichever comes first.

## Running a Simulation Nonstop

The run command lets you run a program from the current point in the simulation to the end, skipping any intervening breakpoints. At the end of the simulation, the debugger returns you to the MATLAB command line. To continue debugging a model, you must restart the debugger.

## Advancing to the Next Block

To advance a simulation one block, click ⊡ on the debugger toolbar or, if the debugger is running in command-line mode, enter step at the debugger prompt. The debugger executes the current block, stops, and highlights the next block in the model's block execution order (see "Displaying a Model's Block Execution Order" on page 8-20). For example, the following figure shows the vdp block diagram after execution of the model's first block.

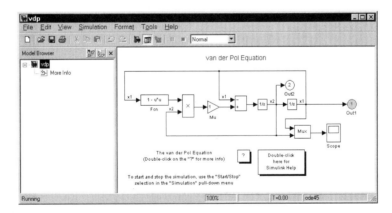

If the next block to be executed occurs in a subsystem block, the debugger opens the subsystem's block diagram and highlights the next block.

After executing a block, the debugger prints the block's inputs (U) and outputs (Y) and redisplays the debug command prompt in the debugger output panel (in GUI mode) or in the MATLAB command window (in command-line mode).

The debugger prompt shows the next block to be evaluated.

```
(sldebug @0:0 'vdp/Integrator1'): step
U1 = [0]
Y1 = [2]
(sldebug @0:1 'vdp/Out1'):
```

### Crossing a Time Step Boundary

After executing the last block in the model's block execution list, the debugger advances the simulation to the next time step and halts the simulation. To signal that you have crossed a time step boundary, the debugger prints the current time in the debugger output panel in GUI mode or in the MATLAB command window in command-line mode. For example, stepping through the last block of the first time step of the vdp model results in the following output in the debugger output panel or the MATLAB command window.

```
(sldebug @0:8 'vdp/Sum'): step
U1 = [2]
U2 = [0]
Y1 = [-2]
[Tm=0.0001004754572603832  ] **Start** of system 'vdp' outputs
```

### Stepping by Minor Time Steps

You can step by blocks within minor time steps, as well as within major steps. To step by blocks within minor time steps, check the **Minor time steps** option on the debugger's **Break on conditions** panel or enter minor at the debugger command prompt.

## Advancing to the Next Time Step

To advance to the next time step, click ⬛ or enter the next command at the debugger command line. The debugger executes the remaining blocks in the current time step and advances the simulation to the beginning of the next time step. For example, entering next after starting the vdp model in debug mode causes the following message to appear in the MATLAB command window.

```
[Tm=0.0001004754572603832  ] **Start** of system 'vdp' outputs
```

# Setting Breakpoints

The Simulink debugger allows you to define stopping points in a simulation called breakpoints. You can then run a simulation from breakpoint to breakpoint, using the debugger's continue command. The debugger lets you define two types of breakpoints: unconditional and conditional. An unconditional breakpoint occurs whenever a simulation reaches a block or time step that you specified previously. A conditional breakpoint occurs when a condition that you specified in advance arises in the simulation.

Breakpoints come in handy when you know that a problem occurs at a certain point in your program or when a certain condition occurs. By defining an appropriate breakpoint and running the simulation via the continue command, you can skip immediately to the point in the simulation where the problem occurs.

You set a breakpoint by clicking the breakpoint button on the debugger toolbar

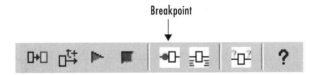
Breakpoint

or checking the appropriate breakpoint conditions (GUI mode)

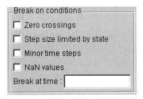

or entering the appropriate breakpoint command (command-line mode).

| Command | Causes Simulation to Stop |
| --- | --- |
| break <gcb \| s:b> | At the beginning of a block |
| bafter <gcb \| s:b> | At the end of a block |

| Command | Causes Simulation to Stop |
|---------|---------------------------|
| tbreak [t] | At a simulation time step |
| nanbreak | At the occurrence of an underflow or overflow (NaN) or infinite (Inf) value |
| xbreak | When the simulation reaches the state that determines the simulation step size |
| zcbreak | When a zero-crossing occurs between simulation time steps |

## Setting Breakpoints at Blocks

The debugger lets you specify a breakpoint at the beginning of the execution of a block or at the end of the execution of a block (command-line mode only).

### Specifying a Breakpoint at the Start of a Block's Execution

Setting a breakpoint at the beginning of a block causes the debugger to stop the simulation when it reaches the block on each time step. You can specify the block on which to set the breakpoint graphically or via a block index in command-line mode. To set a breakpoint graphically at the beginning of a block's execution, select the block in the model window and click ⊕ on the debugger's toolbar or enter

    break gcb

at the debugger command line. To specify the block via its block index (command-line mode only), enter

    break s:b

where s:b is the block's index (see "About Block Indexes" on page 8-6).

---

**Note** You cannot set a breakpoint on a virtual block. A virtual block is a block whose function is purely graphical: it indicates a grouping or relationship among a model's computational blocks. The debugger warns you if you attempt to set a breakpoint on a virtual block. You can obtain a listing of a model's nonvirtual blocks, using the slist command (see "Displaying a Model's Nonvirtual Blocks" on page 8–21).

---

In GUI mode, the debugger's **Break/Display points** panel displays the blocks where breakpoints exist.

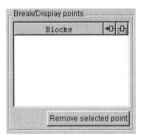

### Setting a Breakpoint at the End of a Block's Execution

In command-line mode, the debugger allows you to set a breakpoint at the end of a block's execution, using the bafter command. As with break, you can specify the block graphically or via its block index.

### Clearing Breakpoints from Blocks

To clear a breakpoint temporarily, uncheck the first check box next to the breakpoint in the **Watch points** panel (GUI mode only). To clear a breakpoint permanently in GUI mode, select the breakpoint in the **Break/Display points** panel and click the **Remove selected point** button. In command-line mode use the clear command to clear breakpoints. You can specify the block by entering its block index or by selecting the block in the model diagram and entering gcb as the argument of the clear command.

## Setting Breakpoints at Time Steps

To set a breakpoint at a time step, enter a time in the debugger's **Stop at time** field (GUI mode) or enter the time, using the tbreak command. This causes the debugger to stop the simulation at the beginning of the first time step that follows the specified time. For example, starting vdp in debug mode and entering the commands

```
tbreak 9
continue
```

causes the debugger to halt the simulation at the beginning of time step 9.0785 as indicated by the output of the continue command.

```
[Tm=9.07847133212036        ] **Start** of system 'vdp' outputs
```

## Breaking on Nonfinite Values

Checking the debugger's **NaN values** option or entering the nanbreak command causes the simulation to stop when a computed value is infinite or outside the range of values that can be represented by the machine running the simulation. This option is useful for pinpointing computational errors in a Simulink model.

## Breaking on Step-Size Limiting Steps

Checking the **Step size limited by state** option or entering the xbreak command causes the debugger to stop the simulation when the model uses a variable-step solver and the solver encounters a state that limits the size of the steps that it can take. This command is useful in debugging models that appear to require an excessive number of simulation time steps to solve.

## Breaking at Zero-Crossings

Checking the **Zero crossings** option or entering the zcbreak command causes the simulation to halt when Simulink detects a non-sampled zero crossing in a model that includes blocks where zero-crossings can arise. After halting, Simulink prints the location in the model, the time, and the type (rising or falling) of the zero-crossing. For example, setting a zero-crossing break at the start of execution of the zeroxing demo model

```
sldebug zeroxing
[Tm=0                    ] **Start** of system 'zeroxing' outputs
(sldebug @0:0 'zeroxing/Sine Wave'): zcbreak
Break at zero crossing events is enabled.
```

and continuing the simulation

```
(sldebug @0:0 'zeroxing/Sine Wave'): continue
```

results in a rising zero-crossing break at

```
[Tm=0.34350110879329        ] Breaking at block 0:2

[Tm=0.34350110879329        ] Rising zero crossing on 3rd zcsignal
in block 0:2 'zeroxing/Saturation'
```

If a model does not include blocks capable of producing nonsampled zero-crossings, the command prints a message advising you of this fact.

# Displaying Information About the Simulation

The Simulink debugger provides a set of commands that allow you to display block states, block inputs and outputs, and other information while running a model.

## Displaying Block I/O

The debugger allows you to display block I/O by selecting the appropriate buttons on the debugger toolbar

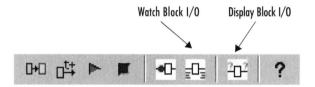

or by entering the appropriate debugger command.

| Command | Displays a Block's I/O |
|---------|------------------------|
| probe | Immediately |
| disp | At every breakpoint |
| trace | Whenever the block executes |

## Displaying I/O of Selected Block

To display the I/O of a block, select the block and click ▦ in GUI mode or enter the probe command in command-line mode.

| Command | Description |
|---------|-------------|
| probe | Enter or exit probe mode. In probe mode, the debugger displays the current inputs and outputs of any block that you select in the model's block diagram. Typing any command causes the debugger to exit probe mode. |
| probe gcb | Display I/O of selected block. |
| probe s:b | Print the I/O of the block specified by system number s and block number b. |

The debugger prints the current inputs and outputs of the selected block in the debugger output pane (GUI mode) or the MATLAB command window.

The probe command comes in handy when you need to examine the I/O of a block whose I/O is not otherwise displayed. For example, suppose you are using the step command to run a model block by block. Each time you step the model, the debugger displays the inputs and outputs of the current block. The probe command lets you examine the I/O of other blocks as well. Similarly, suppose you are using the next command to step through a model by time steps. The next command does not display block I/O. However, if you need to examine a block's I/O after entering a next command, you can do so, using the probe command.

## Displaying Block I/O Automatically at Breakpoints

The disp command causes the debugger to display a specified block's inputs and outputs whenever it halts the simulation. You can specify a block either by entering its block index or by selecting it in the block diagram and entering gcb as the disp command argument. You can remove any block from the debugger's list of display points, using the undisp command. For example, to remove block 0:0, either select the block in the model diagram and enter undisp gcb or simply enter undisp 0:0.

**Note** Automatic display of block I/O at breakpoints is not available in the debugger's GUI mode.

The disp command is useful when you need to monitor the I/O of a specific block or set of blocks as you step through a simulation. Using the disp command, you can specify the blocks you want to monitor and the debugger will then redisplay the I/O of those blocks on every step. Note that the debugger always displays the I/O of the current block when you step through a model block by block, using the step command. So, you do not need to use the disp command if you are interested in watching only the I/O of the current block.

### Watching Block I/O

To watch a block, select the block and click ▣ in the debugger toolbar or enter the trace command. In GUI mode, if a breakpoint exists on the block, you can set a watch on it as well by checking the watch check box for the block in the **Watch points** pane. In command-line mode, you can also specify the block by specifying its block index in the trace command. You can remove a block from the debugger's list of trace points, using the untrace command.

The debugger displays a watched block's I/O whenever the block executes. Watching a block allows you obtain a complete record of the block's I/O without having to stop the simulation.

## Displaying Algebraic Loop Information

The atrace command causes the debugger to display information about a model's algebraic loops (see "Algebraic Loops" on page 3-17) each time they are solved. The command takes a single argument that specifies the amount of information to display.

| Command | Displays for Each Algebraic Loop |
|---------|----------------------------------|
| atrace 0 | No information |
| atrace 1 | The loop variable solution, the number of iterations required to solve the loop, and the estimated solution error |
| atrace 2 | Same as level 1 |

| Command | Displays for Each Algebraic Loop |
|---------|----------------------------------|
| atrace 3 | Level 2 plus the Jacobian matrix used to solve loop |
| atrace 4 | Level 3 plus intermediate solutions of the loop variable |

## Displaying System States

The states debug command lists the current values of the system's states in the MATLAB command window. For example, the following sequence of commands shows the states of the Simulink bouncing ball demo (bounce) after its first and second time-steps.

```
sldebug bounce
[Tm=0                        ] **Start** of system 'bounce' outputs
(sldebug @0:0 'bounce/Position'): states
Continuous state vector (value,index,name):
  10                         0 (0:0 'bounce/Position')
  15                         1 (0:5 'bounce/Velocity')
(sldebug @0:0 'bounce/Position'): next
[Tm=0.01                     ] **Start** of system 'bounce' outputs
(sldebug @0:0 'bounce/Position'): states
Continuous state vector (value,index,name):
  10.1495095                 0 (0:0 'bounce/Position')
  14.9019                    1 (0:5 'bounce/Velocity')
```

## Displaying Integration Information

The ishow command toggles display of integration information. When enabled, this option causes the debugger to print a message each time that the simulation takes a time step or encounters a state that limits the size of a time step. In the first case, the debugger prints the size of the time step, for example,

```
[Tm=9.996264188473381        ] Step of 0.01 was taken by integrator
```

In the second case, the debugger displays the state that currently determines the size of time steps, for example,

```
[Ts=9.676264188473388        ] Integration limited by 1st state of
block 0:0 'bounce/Position'
```

8-19

# Displaying Information About the Model

In addition to providing information about a simulation, the debugger can provide you with information about the model that underlies the simulation.

## Displaying a Model's Block Execution Order

Simulink determines the order in which to execute blocks at the beginning of a simulation run, during model initialization. During simulation, Simulink maintains a list of blocks sorted by execution order. This list is called the sorted list. In GUI mode, the debugger displays the sorted list in its **Execution Order** panel. In command-line mode, the slist command displays the model's block execution order in the MATLAB command window. The list includes the block index for each command.

```
---- Sorted list for 'vdp' [12 blocks, 9 nonvirtual blocks,
directFeed=0]
  0:0     'vdp/Integrator1' (Integrator)
  0:1     'vdp/Out1' (Outport)
  0:2     'vdp/Integrator2' (Integrator)
  0:3     'vdp/Out2' (Outport)
  0:4     'vdp/Fcn' (Fcn)
  0:5     'vdp/Product' (Product)
  0:6     'vdp/Mu' (Gain)
  0:7     'vdp/Scope' (Scope)
  0:8     'vdp/Sum' (Sum)
```

## Displaying a Block

To determine which block in a model's diagram corresponds to a particular index, type bshow s:b at the command prompt, where s:b is the block index. The bshow command opens the system containing the block (if necessary) and selects the block in the system's window.

### Displaying a Model's Nonvirtual Systems

The systems command prints a list of the nonvirtual systems in the model being debugged. For example, the Simulink clutch demo (clutch) contains the following systems.

```
sldebug clutch
[Tm=0                         ] **Start** of system 'clutch' outputs
(sldebug @0:0 'clutch/Clutch Pedal'): systems
  0   'clutch'
  1   'clutch/Locked'
  2   'clutch/Unlocked'
```

**Note** The systems command does not list subsystems that are purely graphical in nature, that is, subsystems that the model diagram represents as Subsystem blocks but which Simulink solves as part of a parent system. In Simulink models, the root system and triggered or enabled subsystems are true systems. All other subsystems are virtual (that is, graphical) and hence do not appear in the listing produced by the systems command.

### Displaying a Model's Nonvirtual Blocks

The slist command displays a list of the nonvirtual blocks in a model. The listing groups the blocks by system. For example, the following sequence of commands produces a list of the nonvirtual blocks in the Van der Pol (vdp) demo model.

```
sldebug vdp
[Tm=0                         ] **Start** of system 'vdp' outputs
(sldebug @0:0 'vdp/Integrator1'): slist
---- Sorted list for 'vdp' [12 blocks, 9 nonvirtual blocks,
directFeed=0]
   0:0    'vdp/Integrator1' (Integrator)
   0:1    'vdp/Out1' (Outport)
   0:2    'vdp/Integrator2' (Integrator)
   0:3    'vdp/Out2' (Outport)
   0:4    'vdp/Fcn' (Fcn)
   0:5    'vdp/Product' (Product)
   0:6    'vdp/Mu' (Gain)
   0:7    'vdp/Scope' (Scope)
   0:8    'vdp/Sum' (Sum)
```

---

**Note** The slist command does not list blocks that are purely graphical in nature, that is, blocks that indicate relationships or groupings among computational blocks.

---

### Displaying Blocks with Potential Zero-Crossings

The zclist prints a list of blocks in which nonsampled zero-crossings can occur during a simulation. For example, zclist prints the following list for the clutch sample model.

```
(sldebug @0:0 'clutch/Clutch Pedal'): zclist
   2:3    'clutch/Unlocked/Sign' (Signum)
   0:4    'clutch/Lockup Detection/Velocities Match' (HitCross)
   0:10   'clutch/Lockup Detection/Required Friction
             for Lockup/Abs' (Abs)
   0:11   'clutch/Lockup Detection/Required Friction for
             Lockup/ Relational Operator' (RelationalOperator)
   0:18   'clutch/Break Apart Detection/Abs' (Abs)
   0:20   'clutch/Break Apart Detection/Relational Operator'
             (RelationalOperator)
   0:24   'clutch/Unlocked' (SubSystem)
   0:27   'clutch/Locked' (SubSystem)
```

### Displaying Algebraic Loops

The ashow command highlights a specified algebraic loop or the algebraic loop that contains a specified block. To highlight a specified algebraic loop, type ashow s#n, where s is the index of the system (see "Displaying a Model's Block Execution Order" on page 8-20) that contains the loop and n is the index of the loop in the system. To display the loop that contains the currently selected block, enter ashow gcb. To show a loop that contains a specified block, type ashow s:b, where s:b is the block's index. To clear algebraic-loop highlighting from the model diagram, enter ashow clear.

### Displaying Debugger Status

In GUI mode, the debugger displays the settings of various debug options, such as conditional breakpoints, in its **Status** panel. In command-line mode, the status command displays debugger settings. For example, the following sequence of commands displays the initial debug settings for the vdp model.

```
sim('vdp',[0,10],simset('debug','on'))
[Tm=0                          ] **Start** of system 'vdp' outputs
(sldebug @0:0 'vdp/Integrator1'): status
  Current simulation time: 0 (MajorTimeStep)
  Last command: ""
  Stop in minor times steps is disabled.
  Break at zero crossing events is disabled.
  Break when step size is limiting by a state is disabled.
  Break on non-finite (NaN,Inf) values is disabled.
  Display of integration information is disabled.
  Algebraic loop tracing level is at 0.
```

# Simulink
# Quick Reference

## Introduction

You can view complete information about any of these blocks from the MATLAB Help Browser:

**1** Select **Using Simulink**.

**2** Scroll down to the **Block Reference** section and select the desired block.

### Continuous Library Blocks

| | |
|---|---|
| Derivative | Output the time derivative of the input. |
| Integrator | Integrate a signal. |
| Memory | Output the block input from the previous time step. |
| State-Space | Implement a linear state-space system. |
| Transfer Fcn | Implement a linear transfer function. |
| Transport Delay | Delay the input by a given amount of time. |
| Variable Transport Delay | Delay the input by a variable amount of time. |
| Zero-Pole | Implement a transfer function specified in terms of poles and zeros. |

### Debugger Commands

| | |
|---|---|
| ashow | Show an algebraic loop. |
| atrace | Set algebraic loop trace level. |
| bafter | Insert a breakpoint after execution of a block. |
| break | Insert a breakpoint before execution of a block. |
| bshow | Show a specified block. |
| clear | Clear a breakpoint from a block. |
| continue | Continue the simulation. |
| disp | Display a block's I/O when the simulation stops. |

### Debugger Commands (Continued)

| | |
|---|---|
| help | Display help for debugger commands. |
| ishow | Enable or disable display of integration information. |
| minor | Enable or disable minor step mode. |
| nanbreak | Set or clear break on nonfinite value. |
| next | Go to start of the next time step. |
| probe | Display a block's I/O. |
| quit | Abort simulation. |
| run | Run the simulation to completion. |
| slist | List a model's nonvirtual blocks. |
| states | Display current state values. |
| status | Display debugging options in effect. |
| step | Step to next block. |
| stop | Stop the simulation. |
| systems | List a model's nonvirtual systems. |
| tbreak | Set or clear a time breakpoint. |
| trace | Display a block's I/O each time it executes. |
| undisp | Remove a block from the debugger's list of display points. |
| untrace | Remove a block from the debugger's list of trace point. |
| xbreak | Break when the debugger encounters a step-size-limiting state. |
| zcbreak | Break at nonsampled zero-crossing events. |
| zclist | List blocks containing nonsampled zero crossings. |

### Discrete Library Blocks

| | |
|---|---|
| Discrete Filter | Implement IIR and FIR filters. |
| Discrete State-Space | Implement a discrete state-space system. |
| Discrete Transfer Fcn | Implement a discrete transfer function. |

## Discrete Library Blocks (Continued)

| | |
|---|---|
| Discrete Zero-Pole | Implement a discrete transfer function specified in terms of poles and zeros. |
| Discrete-Time Integrator | Perform discrete-time integration of a signal. |
| First-Order Hold | Implement a first-order sample-and-hold. |
| Unit Delay | Delay a signal one sample period. |

## Functions & Tables Library Blocks

| | |
|---|---|
| Direct Look-Up Table (n-D) | Index into an N-dimensional table to retrieve a scalar, vector or 2-D matrix. |
| Fcn | Apply a specified expression to the input. |
| Look-Up Table | Perform piecewise linear mapping of the input. |
| Look-Up Table (2-D) | Perform piecewise linear mapping of two inputs. |
| Look-Up Table (n-D) | Perform piecewise linear or spline mapping of two or more inputs. |
| MATLAB Fcn | Apply a MATLAB function or expression to the input. |
| S-Function | Access an S-function. |

## Math Library Blocks

| | |
|---|---|
| Abs | Output the absolute value of the input. |
| Algebraic Constraint | Constrain the input signal to zero. |
| Combinatorial Logic | Implement a truth table. |
| Complex to Magnitude-Angle | Output the phase and magnitude of a complex input signal. |

## Math Library Blocks (Continued)

| | |
|---|---|
| Complex to Real-Imag | Output the real and imaginary parts of a complex input signal. |
| Derivative | Output the time derivative of the input. |
| Dot Product | Generate the dot product. |
| Gain | Multiply block input. |
| Logical Operator | Perform the specified logical operation on the input. |
| Magnitude-Angle to Complex | Output a complex signal from magnitude and phase inputs. |
| Math Function | Perform a mathematical function. |
| Matrix Gain | Multiply the input by a matrix. |
| MinMax | Output the minimum or maximum input value. |
| Product | Generate the product or quotient of block inputs. |
| Real-Imag to Complex | Output a complex signal from real and imaginary inputs. |
| Relational Operator | Perform the specified relational operation on the input. |
| Rounding Function | Perform a rounding function. |
| Sign | Indicate the sign of the input. |
| Slider Gain | Vary a scalar gain using a slider. |
| Sum | Generate the sum of inputs. |
| Trigonometric Function | Perform a trigonometric function. |

## Model Construction Commands

| | |
|---|---|
| add_block | Add a new block to a system. |
| add_line | Add a line to a system. |
| bdroot | Get the name of the root-level system. |
| delete_block | Delete a block from a system. |
| delete_line | Delete a line from a system. |

**A-3**

## Model Construction Commands (Continued)

| | |
|---|---|
| find_system | Find a system, block, line, or annotation. |
| gcb | Get the pathname of the current block. |
| gcbh | Get the handle of the current block. |
| gcs | Get the pathname of the current system. |
| get_param | Get a parameter value. |
| replace_block | Replace a block in a system. |
| set_param | Set parameter values. |
| simulink | Open the Simulink block library. |

## Nonlinear Library Blocks

| | |
|---|---|
| Backlash | Model the behavior of a system with play. |
| Coulomb & Viscous Friction | Model discontinuity at zero, with linear gain elsewhere. |
| Dead Zone | Provide a region of zero output. |
| Manual Switch | Switch between two inputs. |
| Multiport Switch | Choose between block inputs. |
| Quantizer | Discretize input at a specified interval. |
| Rate Limiter | Limit the rate of change of a signal. |
| Relay | Switch output between two constants. |
| Saturation | Limit the range of a signal. |
| Switch | Switch between two inputs. |

## Signals & Systems Library Blocks

| | |
|---|---|
| Bus Selector | Output selected input signals. |
| Configurable Subsystem | Represent any block selected from a specified library. |
| Data Store Memory | Define a shared data store. |
| Bus Selector | Output selected input signals. |

## Signals & Systems Library Blocks (Continued)

| | |
|---|---|
| Configurable Subsystem | Represent any block selected from a specified library. |
| Data Store Memory | Define a shared data store. |
| Data Store Read | Read data from a shared data store. |
| Data Store Write | Write data to a shared data store. |
| Data Type Conversion | Convert a signal to another data type. |
| Demux | Separate a vector signal into output signals. |
| Enable | Add an enabling port to a subsystem. |
| From | Accept input from a Goto block. |
| Goto | Pass block input to From blocks. |
| Goto Tag Visibility | Define the scope of a Goto block tag. |
| Ground | Ground an unconnected input port. |
| Hit Crossing | Detect crossing point. |
| IC | Set the initial value of a signal. |
| Inport | Create an input port for a subsystem or an external input. |
| Merge | Combine several input lines into a scalar line. |
| Model Info | Display revision control information in a model. |
| Mux | Combine several input lines into a vector line. |
| Outport | Create an output port for a subsystem or an external output. |
| Probe | Output an input signal's width, sample time, and/or signal type. |
| Reshape | Change the dimensionality of a signal. |
| Selector | Select or reorder the elements of the input vector. |
| Signal Specification | Specify attributes of a signal. |

## Signals & Systems Library Blocks (Continued)

| | |
|---|---|
| Subsystem | Represent a system within another system. |
| Terminator | Terminate an unconnected output port. |
| Trigger | Add a trigger port to a subsystem. |
| Width | Output the width of the input vector. |

## Sinks Library Blocks

| | |
|---|---|
| Display | Show the value of the input. |
| Scope | Display signals generated during a simulation. |
| Stop Simulation | Stop the simulation when the input is nonzero. |
| To File | Write data to a file. |
| To Workspace | Write data to a matrix in the workspace. |
| XY Graph | Display an X-Y plot of signals using a MATLAB figure window. |

## Sources Library Blocks

| | |
|---|---|
| Band-Limited White Noise | Introduce white noise into a continuous system. |
| Chirp Signal | Generate a sine wave with increasing frequency. |
| Clock | Display and provide the simulation time. |
| Constant | Generate a constant value. |
| Digital Clock | Generate simulation time at the specified sampling interval. |
| Digital Pulse Generator | Generate pulses at regular intervals. |
| From File | Read data from a file. |
| From Workspace | Read data from a matrix defined in the workspace. |

## Sources Library Blocks (Continued)

| | |
|---|---|
| Pulse Generator | Generate pulses at regular intervals. |
| Ramp | Generate a constantly increasing or decreasing signal. |
| Random Number | Generate normally distributed random numbers. |
| Repeating Sequence | Generate a repeatable arbitrary signal. |
| Signal Generator | Generate various waveforms. |
| Sine Wave | Generate a sine wave. |
| Step | Generate a step function. |
| Uniform Random Number | Generate uniformly distributed random numbers. |

**A-5**

# Index